CLARENDON M
TUDOR

Genera

J. A. W. B

Here begynneth the
booke Intituled Ovyde
of Methamorphoseos.
Whiche conteyneth in
some xv. bookes. And
first begynneth the
prologue.

they good or evyll ben
wreton for our prouf
fyt and doctrine. The
good to thende to take
ensample by them to
do well. And the evyll
to thende that we shol

Selections from
WILLIAM CAXTON

With an Introduction, Notes, and
Glossary by

N. F. BLAKE

OXFORD
AT THE CLARENDON PRESS
1973

Oxford University Press, Ely House, London, W. 1
GLASGOW NEW YORK TORONTO MELBOURNE WELLINGTON
CAPE TOWN IBADAN NAIROBI DAR ES SALAAM LUSAKA ADDIS ABABA
DELHI BOMBAY CALCUTTA MADRAS KARACHI LAHORE DACCA
KUALA LUMPUR SINGAPORE HONG KONG TOKYO

Printed in Great Britain
at the University Press, Oxford
by Vivian Ridler
Printer to the University

CONTENTS

INTRODUCTION

It was only as a relatively old man that Caxton embarked on his career as translator and printer. He began his working life as a mercer and merchant adventurer, engaging particularly in the flourishing trade between England and the Low Countries. Wool was the most important commodity handled, but the merchant adventurers also traded in luxury goods. Prominent among such goods were illuminated manuscripts, for at the end of the medieval period the workshops of the Low Countries were the foremost producers in north-west Europe of manuscripts both with and without illustrations. Many fine examples of their work, probably imported during the fifteenth century by merchant adventurers like Caxton, may still be found in English libraries. Caxton took part in this trade and through it he became familiar with the works which were then fashionable in courtly circles. These works were written in French, for the Low Countries then formed part of the duchy of Burgundy. The Dukes increasingly spent their time there rather than in France since the Low Countries formed the richest and most populous part of their domains. It was this wealth that enabled them to maintain in splendour a court which dazzled the rest of Europe. England, linked to the Low Countries by close mercantile ties and ruled by a family with marriage connections with the Burgundian ducal house, could hardly escape the fascination exerted by the Burgundian court. Inevitably the English nobles looked there for their models in dress, behaviour, and literature.

The Burgundian ducal court witnessed what has been called the last flowering of the Middle Ages—and like many late flowerings it was brilliant, vivid, and short-lived. It was also distinctively medieval, for in behaviour and literary taste the court seemed to be scarcely touched by the new humanism that was spreading northwards from Italy. The books in the ducal library, which were almost all in French rather than Latin, consisted principally of courtly romances, histories, and religious works of a non-specialized nature such as lives of saints. Most exhibit a marked nostalgia for the past, albeit a past portrayed in contemporary dress and endowed with contemporary ideas. Men's eyes were directed backwards, for the past was the ideal that the present should emulate; moreover, it was realized symbolically at the court of Burgundy by the establishment of the Order of the Golden Fleece. Such orders embodied all the virtues men attributed to the past, but had no influence or importance in the political conditions of the time.

When Caxton became aware of the possibilities of the printing-press, he decided to capitalize on the good fortune which had brought him to the Low Countries where he was engaged in the trade in manuscripts and where he had dealings with the highest in the land. In his career as merchant adventurer he had risen to be Governor of the English Nation at Bruges, and as such he had become involved in the many complicated diplomatic manoeuvrings that took place between England and the Dukes of Burgundy. He knew many of the chief negotiators on both sides and was probably supplying them with manuscripts in the courtly taste. By printing English translations of these works he could corner the market, for he alone would be able to provide members of the English nobility with reasonably priced books which contained what was currently the most fashionable reading-matter in their own language. It was for this reason that he established his press at Westminster Abbey on his return to England in 1476; there he was conveniently situated for the court and for its members, who were to be his best clients.

Caxton's books were not issued in accordance with any plan; they were produced as the texts became available, for he did not go out of his way to find a particular book to print. Some works were suggested and even translated by his patrons among the nobility; others were translated simply because they happened to be among his stock. And his stock probably changed quite quickly, since he almost certainly continued as a seller of manuscripts after he turned to printing. Since he stocked manuscripts that would appeal to his courtly clients, his printed translations were of the same sort. In fact his publications consist principally of two types: the writings of the courtly poets like Chaucer, Gower, and Lydgate, and English prose translations of French books made by Caxton or his patrons. There are, however, two important exceptions to this general rule. Histories of England, which did not exist in French versions, had to be printed from English manuscripts; and Malory's *Le Morte d'Arthur*, though in part a translation from French, had not been written by one of Caxton's patrons, and he felt in this case that he had to modify its style to make it acceptable to his usual public. Such modification was necessary because of the stylistic expectations current in the fifteenth century. Authors tried at that period to emulate Chaucer's style by using many French loan-words, a complicated syntax, elaborate rhetorical patterns, an aureate vocabulary, and ornate stanza forms. Prose was also expected to conform to the same stylistic prejudices, and to many this meant that the closer an English version was to French, the better its English prose style. Caxton was a child of his age, and as a result he deliberately set out to keep his translations as close to the French as possible. He purposely altered Malory's unique style to make it as close as he could to that of the average French-based romance. Today, we admire Malory's style so much that we criticize Caxton's handling of this text; but we should remember that by fifteenth-century standards it is Malory who is unusual.

In making the selections for this volume I have confined my choice to those texts which were written or translated by Caxton or which, though written by others, were modified by him. As Caxton had no publishing policy, no benefit would have accrued from my setting out the selections chronologically. I have also thought it undesirable to arrange them into arbitrary genres such as romance, history, and religion, since it is doubtful whether Caxton and his contemporaries would have thought of the works in this way. Instead I have organized them broadly in their relation to the past. The two prologues that open the selections are concerned with history and its uses. These are followed by historical passages: first those in chronicle form which concern recent events, then those typifying the presentation of older history as little more than a succession of colourful stories used to illustrate particular moral precepts. History merges into romance, and both genres are used as a vehicle for edification, though the passage from *Reynard the Fox*, a natural pendant to the extract from *Charles the Great*, shows that medieval man could laugh at his own didacticism.

After these, I include examples of classical stories which were adapted to suit medieval tastes. The final passages are taken from collections of stories on which has been imposed either a rigid framework, as in the enumeration of the pieces of a chess game or the Church's calendar, or a more flexible one such as the advice to be offered to young ladies. Whereas, in the earlier pieces, the pattern of history or of classical writers is followed, in the later ones the medieval author establishes his own. But the final result is often much the same. Thus, when the *History of Troy* is read as an allegory, each episode develops a meaning and the whole becomes little more than a collection of disjointed exempla providing different morals, all of which are loosely connected with the story of Troy.

The volume concludes with Caxton's epilogue to the *Order of Chivalry*, which serves to gather together the strands of the previous selections: history, chivalry, and the uses of the past are all to be found here. Caxton's intention is to improve the present by calling to mind the past, and the element of exhortation is a constant feature.

In this as in other ways, Caxton, far from being a herald of the new humanism, embodied and preserved the characteristic features of late medieval culture.

BIOGRAPHICAL NOTE

THE exact date and place of Caxton's birth are uncertain, but he was born in Kent in the period 1415–24. On completing his apprenticeship to a London mercer named Robert Large, he became a merchant adventurer and was engaged in the trade between England and the Low Countries. He prospered, and ultimately became Governor of the English Nation at Bruges, a post he held from about 1462 till about 1471. About 1469 he began translating French texts into English, though his project was delayed for a couple of years by Edward IV's flight from England. Then in 1471 he recommenced his translation of the French *History of Troy* and went to Cologne to learn the art of printing. On his return to Bruges he printed this translation during 1473/4; this was the first book printed in English. While in Bruges, Caxton also printed his translation of the *Game and Play of the Chess* (1475) and four books in French. In 1476 he returned to London and set up his press in the precincts of Westminster Abbey. From then until his death in 1491 he continued to print books for his aristocratic clientele, though his output was occasionally interrupted by political events. The following list, which includes all his major publications, gives some idea of his industry and taste. Starred titles are translations by Caxton.

1473/4	**History of Troy*
1475	**Game and Play of the Chess*
1477	**Jason*
	Dicts or Sayings of the Philosophers (translation by Earl Rivers)
	Chaucer's *Parliament of Fowls*
1478	*Moral Proverbs* (translation by Earl Rivers)
	Chaucer's *Canterbury Tales* (1st edn.; 2nd edn. 1484)
	Chaucer's translation of *De consolatione philosophiae* by Boethius
1480	*Ovid's *Metamorphoses* (no printed version is extant)
	Chronicles of England

1481	**Mirror of the World* **Reynard the Fox* **Siege and Conquest of Jerusalem* A composite volume containing Cicero's *Of Old Age* and *Of Friendship*, and the *Declamation of Noblesse*, the latter two being translations by John Tiptoft, Earl of Worcester
1482	Trevisa's translation of Higden's *Polychronicon* (modernized by Caxton)
1483	**Golden Legend* Gower's *Confessio Amantis* Lydgate's translation of *The Pilgrimage of the Soul*
1484	**Æsop's Fables* **Book of the Knight of the Tower* **Royal Book* **Order of Chivalry* Chaucer's *House of Fame* Chaucer's *Troilus and Criseyde* Lydgate's *Life of Our Lady*
1485	**Charles the Great* **Paris and Vienne* Malory's *Le Morte d'Arthur* (adapted by Caxton)
1487	*Book of Good Manners*
1489	**Blanchardin and Eglantine* **Doctrinal of Sapience* **Feats of Arms* **Four Sons of Aymon*
1490	**Eneydos*
1491	*Book of Divers Ghostly Matters*

TEXTUAL AND BIBLIOGRAPHICAL NOTE

THE copy-text for each extract (with the exception of No. IX) is in each case taken from a single extant copy of Caxton's printed text. The copies used are those in the John Rylands Library, Manchester (Nos. I, II, III, VI, VII, X, XII, XIII, XV, XVI), and the British Museum (Nos. IV, V, VIII, XI, XIV); No. IX is taken from MS. in Magdalene College, Cambridge (now available in facsimile). Details of Caxton's editions and the extant copies are given in S. de Ricci, *A Census of Caxtons* (London, 1909). In the following list the number of each extract is followed by the number the edition has in de Ricci. The figure given after 'No.' in each case denotes the particular copy listed in de Ricci which I have used in this book—*Ia* and II: 49 No. 7; *Ib* and VI: 76 No. 2; III: 46 No. 11; IV: 19 No. 1; V: 87 No. 1; VII: 7 No. 1; VIII: 83 No. 1; X: 3 No. 14; XI: 4 No. 2; XII: 18 No. 4; XIII: 94 No. 6; XIV: 63 No. 1; XV: 98 No. 1; XVI: 81 No. 2.

The spelling of the original texts has been retained except as follows. The pairs *i/j* and *u/v* are respelt in accordance with modern usage: *unyversal* (not *vnyuersal*). The letter *ȝ* is replaced by *gh* or *z*; *ought* (for *ouȝt*) and *Nyz* (for *Nyȝ*). Initial *ff-* is disregarded. The capitalization, paragraphs, and modern punctuation are the editor's; no apostrophe is used in the genitive case, as this is unnecessary where the texts have *-es* or *-is*. Word-division has been modernized, and Caxton's chapter headings have not been included.

All abbreviations are expanded silently. Obvious typographical mistakes are likewise corrected silently. These mistakes are normally of three types: a turned letter; the repetition of a word at the beginning of the next line or page; and the misplacing of letters, such as spelling *marchaunt* as *mrachaunt*. Where a simple word, letter(s), or abbreviation is missing in the text, this has been supplied in square brackets. Other corrections and departures from the text are recorded in footnotes.

Place-names have been joined together or separated in accordance with modern usage: *Westmestre* (not *west mestre*) and *London Brydge* (not *Londonbrydge*). Some word-groups which are written as two or more words in Caxton but which appear as one word in modern English have not been joined into a single word in those cases in which the constituent elements were still thought of as meaningful parts. Thus in *in dede*, the *in* still retained its prepositional meaning, and appears as an independent word in this instance.

Italics (used for book-titles, etc.) are editorial.

In editing the manuscript in extract No. IX, I have expanded the abbreviations *þ*^{t} and *w*^{t} as *that* and *with* respectively, and in addition to the standardization of *u*/*v* and *i*/*j*, I have replaced *þ* by *th*. There are two types of stroke found above some words, and in dealing with these I have followed the practice of the editors of the Shakespeare Head edition (1924) of the last six books of Caxton's. Only the thick heavy stroke, usually standing for a nasal, is expanded; the thin hairline one (except in *tribulacions* (l. 5) where it stands for the second *i*) has been disregarded. Strokes of a different type over *vaynquysshed* (l. 113), *vylayne* (l. 240), *sholde* (l. 241), and *fel* (l. 304) have also been disregarded. I have expanded as *e* a little tick which appears after final *r*, *g*, and *k*, though some examples are ambiguous; its rare occurrence after other letters is disregarded. I have expanded the final flourish as *-is* in *inconveniencis* (l. 5) and *instrumentis* (l. 52).

Of the books printed by Caxton, the following have been edited in modern times under the aegis of the Early English Text Society: *Book of Courtesy* (ed. F. J. Furnivall, 1868), *Charles the Great* (ed. S. J. H. Herrtage, 1880–1), *Four Sons of Aymon* (ed. O. Richardson, 1884–5), *The Curial* (ed. P. Meyer and F. J. Furnivall, 1888), *Blanchardin and Eglantine* (ed. L. Kellner, 1890), *Eneydos* (ed. M. T. Culley and F. J. Furnivall, 1890), *The Siege and Conquest of Jerusalem* (ed. M. N. Colvin, 1893), *Vocabulary in French and English* (ed. H. Bradley, 1900), *The Rule of St. Benet* (ed. E. A. Kock, 1902), *Mirror of the World* (ed. O. H. Prior,

1913), *Jason* (ed. J. Munro, 1913), *Order of Chivalry* (ed. A. T. P. Byles, 1926), *Feats of Arms* (ed. A. T. P. Byles, 1932), *Paris and Vienne* (ed. MacEdward Leach, 1957), *Reynard the Fox* (ed. N. F. Blake, 1970), and *Book of the Knight of the Tower* (ed. M. Y. Offord, 1971). The Society also published a collection of Caxton' prologues and epilogues edited by W. J. B. Crotch in 1928.

Other modern editions include: *Game and Play of the Chess* (ed. W. E. A. Axon, London, 1883), *Le Morte d'Arthur* (ed. H. O. Sommer, London, 1889–1900), *Golden Legend* (ed. F. S. Ellis, London, 1892), *History of Troy* (ed. H. O. Sommer, London, 1894), *Of Old Age* (ed. H. Susebach, Halle, 1933), *The Cordial* (ed. J. A. Mulders, Nijmegen, n.d.), and *Æsop's Fables* (ed. R. T. Lenaghan, Cambridge, Mass., 1967). Many of Caxton's publications have been issued in facsimile editions in the nineteenth and twentieth centuries, and the complete text of his translation of Ovid's *Metamorphoses* was published in facsimile in 1968 (New York). For further reading the following books are recommended:

BIOGRAPHICAL AND LITERARY

N. S. Aurner, *Caxton: Mirrour of Fifteenth-Century Letters* (London, 1926).

H. S. Bennett, *Chaucer and the Fifteenth Century* (Oxford, 1947).

—— *English Books and Readers 1475 to 1557* (Cambridge, 1952).

N. F. Blake, *Caxton and his World* (London, 1969).

H. R. Plomer, *William Caxton 1421–1491* (London and Boston, 1925).

M. Schlauch, *Antecedents of the English Novel 1400–1600 (from Chaucer to Deloney)* (Warsaw and London, 1963).

TYPOGRAPHICAL

C. F. Bühler, *The Fifteenth-Century Book* (Philadelphia, 1960).

W. and L. Hellinga, *The Fifteenth-Century Printing Types of the Low Countries* (Amsterdam, 1966).

LANGUAGE

R. R. Aurner, 'Caxton and the English Sentence', *University of Wisconsin Studies in Language and Literature*, xviii (1923), 23–59.

N. F. Blake, 'Caxton's Language', *Neuphilologische Mitteilungen*, lxvii (1966), 122–32.

A. O. Sandved, *Studies in the Language of Caxton's Malory and that of the Winchester Manuscript* (Oslo and New York, 1968).

H. Wiencke, *Die Sprache Caxtons* (Leipzig, 1930).

CAXTON AND MALORY

S. Shaw, 'Caxton and Malory', *Essays on Malory*, edited by J. A. W. Bennett (Oxford, 1963), pp. 114–45.

E. Vinaver, *The Works of Sir Thomas Malory*, 2nd edn. (3 vols., Oxford, 1967).

ACKNOWLEDGEMENTS

I OWE thanks to the officials of the John Rylands Library, Manchester, and of the British Museum for providing me with xerox copies of incunabula in their care. The illustration from Caxton's Ovid is reproduced by permission of the Master and Fellows of Magdalene College, Cambridge.

I am indebted to Mrs. M. Y. Offord for her assistance throughout the preparation of this volume and to Professor J. A. W. Bennett for his help with it.

NOTE TO FRONTISPIECE

THIS is the first of the coloured drawings found in the first part of the Magdalene MS. of Caxton's Ovid (*v.* p. 131) and illustrates the prologue to that work. The other three completed pictures represent scenes from the *Metamosphoses*; blank spaces ($5\frac{1}{2}'' \times 5''$) were left at the head of each book for similar illustrations.

The two books (coloured red and blue in the MS.) apparently represent the two volumes in which the English version is found.

A descriptive analysis of the picture will be found in the Sotheby Sale Catalogue, *Bibliotheca Phillippica*, New Series, part II, 27–28 June 1966, p. 13. Kathleen Scott will discuss the identity of the artist in a forthcoming essay.

SELECTIONS

1. Prologues: (*a*) Polychronicon (1482)

GRETE thankynges, lawde and honoure we merytoryously ben bounde to yelde and offre unto wryters of hystoryes, whiche gretely have prouffyted oure mortal lyf, that shewe unto the reders and herers by the ensamples of thynges passyd what thynge is to be desyred and what is to be eschewed. For those thynges 5 whiche oure progenytours [dyde] by the taste of bytternes and experyment of grete jeopardyes have enseygned, admonested and enformed us, excluded fro suche peryllys, to knowe what is prouffytable to oure lyf and acceptable and what is unprouffyt-able and to be refused. He is and ever hath ben reputed the wysest 10 whiche by the experyence of adverse fortune hath byholden and seen the noble cytees, maners and variaunt condycions of the people of many dyverse regyons, for in hym is presupposed the lore of wysedome and polycye by the experyment of jeopardyes and peryllys, whiche have growen of folye in dyverse partyes 15 and contrayes. Yet he is more fortunat and may be reputed as wyse yf he gyve attendaunce withoute tastynge of the stormes of adversyte, that may by the redyng of historyes conteynyng dyverse customes, condycyons, lawes and actes of sondry nacions come unto the knowleche of and understandynge of the same 20 wysedom and polycye. In whiche hystoryes so wreton in large and aourned volumes he syttynge in his chambre or studye maye rede, knowe and understande the polytyke and noble actes of alle the worlde as of one cyte, and the conflyctes, errours, troubles and vexacions done in the sayd unyversal worlde in suche wyse 25 as he had ben and seen them in the propre places where as they were done. For certayne it is a greete beneurte unto a man that can be reformed by other and straunge mennes hurtes and scathes, and by the same to knowe what is requysyte and prouffytable for his lyf and eschewe suche errours and inconvenytys by whiche 30

other men have ben hurte and lost theyr felycyte. Therfore the counseylles of auncyent and whyteheeryd men in whome olde age hath engendryd wysedome ben gretely preysed of yonger men. And yet hystoryes soo moche more excelle them as the
35 dyuturnyte or length of tyme includeth moo ensamples of thynges and laudable actes than th'age of one man may suffyse to see.

Historyes ought not only to be juged moost proffytable to yonge men, whiche by the lecture, redyng and understandyng
40 make them semblable and equale to men of greter age, and to old men to whome longe lyf hath mynystred experymentes of dyverse thynges; but also th'ystoryes able and make ryght pryvate men digne and worthy to have the governaunce of empyres and noble royammes. Historyes moeve and withdrawe
45 emperours and kynges fro vycious tyrannye, fro vecordyous sleuthe unto tryumphe and vyctorye in puyssaunt bataylles. Historyes also have moeved ryght noble knyghtes to deserve eternal laude, whiche foloweth them for their vyctoryous merytes, and cause them more valyantly to entre in jeopardyes of
50 batayles for the defence and tuicion of their countrey and publyke wele. Hystorye also affrayeth cruel tyrauntys for drede of infamye and shame infynyte, bycause of the detestable actes of suche cruel personnes ben oftymes plantyd and regystred in cronykes unto theyr perpetuel obprobrye and dyvulgacion of theyr infamye,
55 as th'actes of Nero and suche other. Truly many of hye and couragyous men of grete empryse desyryng theyr fame to be perpetuelly conservyd by lyteral[1] monumentis, whiche ben the permanente recordes of every vyrtuouse and noble acte, have buylded and edefyed ryall and noble cytees, and for the conserva-
60 cion of the wele publycke have mynystred and establysshed dyscrete and prouffytable lawes. And thus the pryncipal laude and cause of delectable and amyable thynges in whiche mannes felycyte stondeth and resteth ought and maye wel be attributed to hystoryes.

65 Whiche worde historye may be descryved thus. Historye is a perpetuel conservatryce of thoos thynges that have be doone

[1] lyberal

before this presente tyme and also a cotydyan wytnesse of bienfayttes, of malefaytes, grete actes and tryumphal vyctoryes of all maner peple. And also yf the terryble, feyned fables of poetes have moche styred and moeved men to pyte and conservynge 70 of justyce, how moche more is to be supposed that historye, assertryce of veryte and as moder of alle philosophye moevynge our maners to vertue, reformeth and reconcyleth ner hande alle thoos men whiche thurgh the infyrmyte of oure mortal nature hath ledde the mooste parte of theyr lyf in ocyosyte and my- 75 spended theyr tyme, passed ryght soone oute of remembraunce; of whiche lyf and deth is egal oblyvyon. The fruytes of vertue ben inmortall, specyally whanne they ben wrapped in the benefyce of hystoryes.

Thenne it muste folowe that it is mooste fayre to men mortalle 80 to suffre labours and payne for glorye and fame inmortalle. Hercules whan he lyved suffryd greete laboures and peryllys, wylfully puttyng hym self in many terryble and ferdful jeopardyes to obteyne of all peple the benefaytes of inmortal laude and renommee. We rede of other noble men, somme lordes and 85 somme other of lower astates, reputed as goddes in dyverse regyons, the whos famous actes and excellent vertues only hystorye hath preservyd fro perysshyng in eternal memorye. Other monymentes, distributed in dyverse chaunges, enduren but for a short tyme or season. But the vertu of historye dyffused 90 and spredd by the unyversal worlde hath tyme, whiche consumeth all other thynges, as conservatryce and kepar of her werke.

Ferthermore eloquence is soo precious and noble that almooste noo thyng can be founden more precious than it. By eloquence the Grekes ben preferryd in contynuel honour tofore the rude 95 barbares. Oratours and lerned clerkes in like wise excelle unlerned and brutyssh peple. Syth this eloquence is suche that causeth men emonge them self somme t'excelle other after the qualyte of the vertue and eloquence, [it may] be seyn to be of valew. For somme we juge to be good men, digne of laude, whiche shewe to us the 100 waye of vertue. And other have taken another waye: for t'enflamme more [to playsyr] the courages of men by fables of poesye than to prouffyte, and by the lawes and institutes more to punysshe

than to teche. Soo that of thyse thynges the utylyte is myxt with
105 harme; for somme sothly techyth to lye. But historye represent-
ynge the thynges lyke unto the wordes enbraceth al utylyte and
prouffite. It sheweth honeste and maketh vyces detestable. It
enhaunceth noble men and depresseth wicked men and fooles.
Also thynges that historye descryveth by experyence moche
110 prouffyten unto a ryghtful lif.

Thenne syth historye is so precious and also prouffytable, I have
delybered to wryte twoo bookes notable retenyng in them many
noble historyes, as the lyves, myracles, passyons and deth of
dyverse hooly sayntes, whiche shal be comprysed by th'ayde and
115 suffraunce of almyghty God in one of them, whiche is named
Legenda Aurea, that is the *Golden Legende*. And that other book is
named *Polycronycon*, in whiche book ben comprised briefly many
wonderful historyees: fyrst, the descripcion of the universal
world, as wel in lengthe as in brede, with the divisions of
120 countrees, royammes and empyres, the noble cytees, hye mount-
ayns, famous ryvers, merveylles and wondres; and also, the
historial actes and wonderful dedes syth the fyrst makyng of
heven and erth unto the begynnyng of the regne of Kyng
Edward the fourth and unto the yere of Our Lord mcccclx; as by
125 th'ayde of almyghty God shal folowe al alonge after the composynge and gaderynge of Dan Ranulph, monke of Chestre,
fyrste auctour of this book; and afterward englisshed by one
Trevisa, vycarye of Barkley, which atte request of one Sir
Thomas, Lord Barkley, translated this sayd book, the Byble and
130 Bartylmew *De Proprietatibus Rerum* out of Latyn into Englyssh;
and now at this tyme symply emprynted and sette in forme by
me, William Caxton, and a lytel embelysshed fro th'olde makyng.
And also have added suche storyes as I coude fynde fro th'ende
that the said Ranulph fynysshed his book, which was the yere of
135 Our Lord mccclvij, unto the yere of the same mcccclx, whiche ben
an honderd and thre yere. Whiche werke I have finysshed under
the noble protection of my most drad, naturel and soverayne
lord and moost cristen Kynge, Kyng Edward the fourth, humbly
besechyng his moost noble grace to pardone me yf ony thynge
140 be sayd therynne of ignoraunce or other wyse than it ought to

be, and also requyryng al other to amende wher as ther is defaute, wherin he or they may deserve thank and meryte. And I shal praye for them that soo doo, for I knowleche myn ignoraunce and also symplenes. And yf ther be thyng that may plese or prouffite ony man, I am glad that I have achieved it. . . . 145

(*b*) **Le Morte d'Arthur** (1485)

AFTER that I had accomplysshed and fynysshed dyvers hystoryes, as wel of contemplacyon as of other hystoryal and worldly actes of grete conquerours and prynces, and also certeyn bookes of ensaumples and doctryne, many noble and dyvers gentylmen of thys royame of Englond camen and demaunded me many and 5 oftymes wherfore that I have not do made and enprynte the noble hystorye of the Saynt Greal and of the moost renomed crysten Kyng, fyrst and chyef of the thre best crysten and worthy, Kyng Arthur, whyche ought moost to be remembred emonge us Englysshemen tofore al other crysten kynges. For it is notoyrly 10 knowen thorugh the unyversal world that there been ix worthy and the best that ever were: that is to wete thre paynyms, thre jewes and thre crysten men. As for the paynyms they were tofore the incarnacyon of Cryst, whiche were named: the fyrst, Hector of Troye of whome th'ystorye is comen bothe in balade and in 15 prose; the second, Alysaunder the grete; and the thyrd, Julyus Cezar, emperour of Rome, of whome th'ystoryes ben wel kno and had. And as for the thre jewes, whyche also were tofore th'yncarnacyon of our Lord, of whome the fyrst was Duc Josue whyche brought the chyldren of Israhel into the londe of byheste; 20 the second, Davyd, Kyng of Jherusalem; and the thyrd, Judas Machabeus. Of these thre the Byble reherceth al theyr noble hystoryes and actes. And sythe the sayd incarnacyon have ben thre noble crysten men stalled and admytted thorugh the unyversal world into the nombre of the ix beste and worthy. Of 25 whome was fyrst the noble Arthur, whos noble actes I purpose to wryte in thys present book here folowyng. The second was Charlemayn or Charles the grete, of whome th'ystorye is had in

many places bothe in Frensshe and Englysshe. And the thyrd and
30 last was Godefray of Boloyn, of whos actes and lyf I made a book unto th'excellent prynce and kyng of noble memorye, Kyng Edward the fourth. The sayd noble jentylmen instantly requyred me t'emprynte th'ystorye of the sayd noble kyng and conquerour, Kyng Arthur, and of his knyghtes wyth th'ystorye of the Saynt
35 Greal and of the deth and endyng of the sayd Arthur, affermyng that I ought rather t'enprynte his actes and noble feates than of Godefroye of Boloyne or ony of the other eyght, consyderyng that he was a man borne wythin this royame and Kyng and Emperour of the same and that there ben in Frensshe dyvers and
40 many noble volumes of his actes and also of his knyghtes. To whome I answerd that dyvers men holde oppynyon that there was no suche Arthur and that alle suche bookes as been maad of hym ben but fayned and fables bycause that somme cronycles make of hym no mencyon ne remembre hym noo thynge ne of
45 his knyghtes. Wherto they answerd, and one in specyal sayd, that in hym that shold say or thynke that there was never suche a kyng callyd Arthur myght wel be aretted grete folye and blyndenesse, for he sayd that there were many evydences of the contrarye. Fyrst, ye may see his sepulture in the monasterye of Glastyng-
50 burye; and also, in *Polycronycon* in the v book, the syxte chappytre and in the seventh book, the xxiij chappytre where his body was buryed and after founden and translated into the sayd monasterye. Ye shal se also in th'ystorye of Bochas, in his book *De Casu Principum*, parte of his noble actes and also of his falle; also,
55 Galfrydus in his Brutysshe book recounteth his lyf. And in dyvers places of Englond many remembraunces ben yet of hym and shall remayne perpetuelly and also of his knyghtes. Fyrst, in the Abbey of Westmestre at Saynt Edwardes shryne remayneth the prynte of his seal in reed waxe closed in beryll, in whych is
60 wryton *Patricius Arthurus Britannie Gallie Germanie Dacie Imperator*. Item, in the castel of Dover ye may see Gauwayns skulle and Cradoks mantel, at Wynchester the rounde table, in other places Launcelottes swerde and many other thynges. Thenne al these thynges consydered there can no man resonably gaynsaye but
65 there was a kyng of thys lande named Arthur, for in al places

crysten and hethen he is reputed and taken for one of the ix worthy and the fyrst of the thre crysten men. And also he is more spoken of beyonde the see, moo bookes[1] made of his noble actes than there be in Englond, as wel in Duche, Ytalyen, Spaynysshe and Grekysshe as in Frensshe. And yet of record remayne in 70 wytnesse of hym in Wales in the toune of Camelot the grete stones and mervayllous werkys of yron lyeng under the grounde and ryal vautes, which dyvers now lyvyng hath seen. Wherfor it is a mervayl why he is no more renomed in his owne contreye, sauf onelye it accordeth to the word of God whyche sayth that 75 no man is accept for a prophete in his owne contreye. Thenne al these thynges forsayd aledged, I coude not wel denye but that there was suche a noble kyng named Arthur and reputed one of the ix worthy and fyrst and chyef of the cristen men. And many noble volumes be made of hym and of his noble knyghtes in 80 Frensshe which I have seen and redde beyonde the see, which been not had in our maternal tongue. But in Walsshe ben many and also in Frensshe and somme in Englysshe, but nowher nygh alle. Wherfore suche as have late ben drawen oute bryefly into Englysshe, I have after the symple connyng that God hath sente 85 to me, under the favour and correctyon of al noble lordes and gentylmen, enprysed to enprynte a book of the noble hystoryes of the sayd Kynge Arthur and of certeyn of his knyghtes after a copye unto me delyverd. Whyche copye Syr Thomas Malorye dyd take oute of certeyn bookes of Frensshe and reduced it into 90 Englysshe. And I accordyng to my copye have doon sette it in enprynte to the entente that noble men may see and lerne the noble actes of chyvalrye, the jentyl and vertuous dedes that somme knyghtes used in tho dayes by whyche they came to honour, and how they that were vycious were punysshed and ofte put to 95 shame and rebuke; humbly bysechyng al noble lordes and ladyes wyth al other estates of what estate or degree they been of that shal see and rede in this sayd book and werke that they take the good and honest actes in their remembraunce and to folowe the same, wherin they shalle fynde many joyous and playsaunt 100 hystoryes and noble and renomed actes of humanyte, gentylnesse

[1] boookes

and chyvalryes. For herein may be seen noble chyvalrye, curtosye, humanyte, frendlynesse, hardynesse, love, frendshyp, cowardyse, murdre, hate, vertue and synne. Doo after the good and leve the
105 evyl and it shal brynge you to good fame and renommee. And for to passe the tyme thys book[1] shal be plesaunte to rede in. But for to gyve fayth and byleve that al is trewe that is conteyned herin, ye be at your lyberte. But al is wryton for our doctryne and for to beware that we falle not to vyce ne synne, but t'excer-
110 syse and folowe vertu, by whyche we may come and atteyne to good fame and renomme in thys lyf and after thys shorte and transytorye lyf to come unto everlastyng blysse in heven, the whyche He graunte us that reygneth in heven, the blessyd Trynyte. Amen.

II. **Polychronicon: Liber Ultimus** (1482)

Selections from the life of Richard II

AFTER Kyng Edward the thyrd regned Rychard the second that was the noble Prynce Edwardes sone of Wales, which Kyng Rychard was borne at Bourdeux. He was crouned at Westmestre
[1377] the enleventh yere of his age. . . .
[1380] In the thyrdde yere of his regne cam certayne galeyes of warre
6 oute of Fraunce into dyverse portis of Englond and robbed, brente and slue moche peple, in so moche that they cam to Gravysende and brente a grete part of the toune.

In the same yere was ordeyned at a parlement at Westmynstre
10 that every man and woman past fourtene yere of age shold paye to the talage four pens, wherfor fyl afterward moch meschyef.
[1381] For in the fourth yere of his regne the comons aroos in dyverse partyes in Englond and dyde moche harme; and it was callyd the hurlyng tyme. And they of Kente and of Estsex made hem two
15 capytayns callyd Jac Strawe and Watte Tyler, and they assembled on Blacheth. And on Corpus Cristi day they cam into Southwerk

[1] boook

and lete oute all the prysoners of the Kynges Benche and Marchalsee; and cam into London and robbed alle the alyens and straungers, and sloughe and made havoke. On the morne after they cam to the Toure of London where the Kynge was presente 20 the same tyme and toke oute the Archebisshop of Caunterbury and the Pryour of Saynt Johans and a Whyte Frere, confessour to the Kyng, and smote of theyr hedes atte Tour Hyll. Thenne come they ageyne to London and slewe men of lawe and other worthy men in dyverse partyes of the toune. Thenne wente they 25 to the Duc of Lancastres place callyd Savoye and destroyed it doune and bare awey the goodes that they might fynde and brente the place. Thenne wente they to Westmestre and Saynt Martyns the graunt and delyverd them all oute of sayntuarye that were therynne for ony maner grythe. Thenne cam they to the Temples 30 and to alle other Innes of men of lawe and despoylled and brente theyr bookes. Thenne came they to London ageyne and toke oute al the prysonners, felons and other, oute of Newgate and both countours and destroyed theyr bookes.

Thenne on the Monday Kyng Rychard sent for the Mayr of 35 London, William Walworth, and his aldermen and they wente to speke and knowe th'entencion of thyse rebellous peple. Thenne this Jac Strawe lete make an oye in the felde that all his peple shold come nere and here his crye and wyll. Thenne the lordes, the mayer and aldermen havyng indignacion of his presumpcion 40 and covetyse, and the mayer seenge that he dyd noo reverence to the Kynge starte to hym and slewe the sayd Jac Straw, capytayne of the rebellys. And anone his hede was smyten of and the hede reysed up that all myght see hit. And forthwith incontynent alle tho rysers and mysgoverned peple fledde awey. 45 Thenne the Kyng forthwith dubbyd the mayer knyght and fyve of his bretheren aldermen. . . . And after this as they myght take and gete thyse rebellys and mysgoverned people, they henge hem up by ten, by twelve, twenty &c. . . .

This yere Johan Hynde beynge that tyme Mayer of London [1392] and Johan Shadeworth and Henry Vanner shereves were dys- 51 charged[1] of theyr offyces byfore Saynt Johans day Baptyst. And

[1] dysharged

the Kyng seased the fraunchyse and lybertees of the cyte of London and ordeyned and constitued Syr Edward Dalyngredge 55 wardeyn of the cyte; and endured in his offyce unto the fyrst day of Juyll, the yere xvj. And thenne Syr Bowdwyn Radyngton was made wardeyne to Saynt Symons daye and Jude. The cause therof was for a bakers man beryng a basket with horsbrede into Flete Strete. There come a man of the Bisshop of Salesburyes that toke 60 oute an horsloof oute of the baskette, wherfore the bakers man strove with the yoman soo that the Bisshops man brake the bakers mans heede. Thenne neyghbours come aboute to have rescowed hym and to have arestyd the Bisshops man; but he scope fro hem into his lordes place. The constable cam and wold have had hym 65 out, but they withynne the place kept it that they myght not come in. And thenne come the mayer with moche peple and sayde they wold have hym oute or brenne the place and all that were therin. The Bisshop, beynge Tresorer of Englonde, and the Archebisshop of Caunterbury wente togeder to Wyndesore to 70 the Kynge and made a grete complaynte to the Kyng and his counseylle of the cyte of London. And the Kynge sente for the mayer and shereves and yaf hem grete rebukes for th'offence that they hadde done ageynst hym and his offycers in his chambre of London. And deposed the mayer and shereves and made a 75 wardeyne of the cyte, as afore is sayd.

[1393] In the syxtenth yere the Kyng withdrewe his courtes from Westmynstre to Yorke, whiche were there holden and kepte fro the feste of Saynt Johan Baptyst unto Crystemasse after. Thenne atte requeste of the goode Quene Anne and of the Bisshop of 80 London, thenne callyd Gravesende, the Kyng graunted the fraunchyse and lybertees to the cyte of London. And they of London gaf to Seynt Edwards shryne a table of sylver and enameled stondyng on the awter. And after this the mayer, aldermen and sherevys mette with the Kyng submyttynge them 85 humbly to hym as they ought do, and resseyvyng the Kyng thurgh the cyte with grete tryumphe and brought hym to Westmynstre. And on the morne after the mayer, aldermen and shreves presentyng the sayd table and other yeftes prayd the Kynge of his good and speciall grace to have theyr lybertees

and fraunchyses as they hadde tofore tyme. And soo the 90
Kyng graunted to them alle theyr askynge, and wente home
ageyne. . . .

In the nynetenthe yere of Kyng Rychard, he wente to Calays [1396]
and maryed there Quene Isabel, the Kynges doughter of Fraunce.
At whiche tyme the Frensshe lordes were sworen on a booke that 95
alle covenauntes, forwardys and composicions ordeyned and
made on both sydes shold be truly holden and kept withoute
contradiction or dylaye in ony maner wyse. And whanne this
ryal maryage was done and fynysshed Kynge Rychard with Dame
Isabel his Quene cam into Englond. And the Mayer of London 100
with all his bretheren with grete multitude of the comons of the
cyte and the craftys resseyved hem worshipfully atte Blacheth
and brought hem to Saynt Georges Barre; and there takynge
theyr leve, the Kynge and the Quene roode to Kenyngton. And
after that withynne a whyle the Quene cam to the Toure of 105
London, at whoos comyng was moche harme done, for on
London Brydge were nyne personnes crowded to deth, of whome
the Pryour of Typtre was one. And from the Tour she wente
thurgh the cyte of London to Westmynstre, and there she was
crowned. 110

And after this Kyng Rychard by appoyntemente delyverd the
toun of Brest to the Duc of Brytayne, wherof bygon moche
trouble and sorowe whiche dured unto his deth. In the twentyest [1397]
yere Kyng Rychard dyde holde a grete feste at Westmynstre, at
whiche feste arryved the sowdyours that hadde kepte Breste and 115
sate atte dyner in the hall. And after dyner the Duc of Gloucetre
sayd to the Kynge: 'Syre, have ye not seen tho felawes that sate
at dyner in your halle?' And the Kynge demaunded who they
were. And he sayd: 'These ben youre folk that have servyd yow
and ben come from Breste, and now wote not what to doo and 120
have ben evyl payd.' Thenne the Kynge sayd that they shal be
payed. Thenne answerd the Duc of Gloucetre in a grete furye:
'Syre, ye ought fyrste to putte youre bodye in devoyre to gete a
toune or a castel by fayt of warre upon your enemyes er ye sholde
selle or delyver ony townes that your predecessours, kynges of 125
Englond, have goten and conquerd.' To the whiche the Kynge

answerd ryght angrely: 'How saye ye that?' Thenne the Duk his uncle sayd it ageyn. Thenne the Kynge byganne to wexe wrothe and sayde: 'Wene ye that I be a marchaunt or a foole to
130 selle my londe? By Saynt Johan Baptist, nay! But trouthe it is that our cosyn of Britayne hath rendryd and payd to us the somme that my predecessours hadde lente uppon the sayd toune of Brest. And syth he hath payed, it is reasonne that this toune be delyverd to hym ageyne.' Thus beganne the wrath bytwene the Kynge
135 and his uncle.

And afterward at Arondele was a counseylle of certayne lordes, as the Duck of Gloucetre, the Archebisshop of Caunterbury, the Erles of Arondele, Warwyk and Marchal, and other, for to refourme the rewle aboute the Kynge. Whiche lordes promysed
140 eche t'abyde by other and soo departed. And anone after the Erle Marchal, whiche was capytayne of Calays, bewrayed and lete the Kynge have knowleche of all theyr counseylle. Wherupon the fyve and twentyest daye of August the Duke of Gloucetre was arrestyd at Plasshey in Estsex and brought to the Tour of
145 London and from thennes sente to Calays and there murthred and slayne withoute processe of lawe or justyce. And th'Erle of Arondel, the Erle of Warwyk, Syr Johan Cobham, Syre Johan Cheyne knyghtes were arestyd and putte in holde, save th'Erle of Arondel fonde seurte t'answere and wente at large tyl the
[1398] parlement tyme. In the one and twentyest yere of Kyng Rycharde
151 at the parlement holden at Westmynstre th'Erle of Arondel was brought tofore alle the lordes and there was juged to deth, that he sholde goo on fote fro Westmynstre thurgh the cyte of London to the Tour Hylle and there to have his heede smyten of.
155 And syxe lordes roode with hym to see that execucion sholde be doo with grete multitude of peple of men of armes and archers, for they dredde leste he shold be rescowed by men of London. And on the morne th'Archebisshop of Caunterbury, his broder, was banysshed for evermore, and Syre Thomas Mortemer was
160 banysshed also. And Syre Rychard, Erle of Warwyck, cam tofore the parlemente and was juged to the same deth, but bycause of his age he was releced to perpetuel prysonne. The Mondaye after Syre Johan Cobham and Syre Johan Cheyne were juged to be

drawen and hanged, but at the instaunce of the lordes that jugement was releced unto perpetuel prysonne. . . . 165

In the same yere fylle a greete debate and dyssencyon bytwene the Duck of Herford, Erle of Derby, on that one partye and the Duke of Norfolke, Erle Marchal, on that other partye, in so moche that they waged bataylle and caste doune theyr gloves, whiche were taken up byfore the Kynge and ensealed; and the 170 daye and place assygned at Coventre. To whiche place the Kynge cam, the Duk of Lancastre and other lordes. And whanne bothe partyes were in the felde redy for to fyghte, the Kynge toke the matere in his owne honde and forthwyth he exyled and banysshed the Duke of Herford for ten yere and the Duke of Norfolke for 175 ever. The Duc of Norfolcke deyde at Venyse.

In the two and twentyest yere of Kyng Rychard there were [1399] made blank charters to whiche all the ryche men of the royamme were compellyd to sette to theyr seales. And it was noysed thurgh the royamme that he hadde sette Englond to ferme to Syre 180 William Scrope, Erle of Wylshyre, Sir Johan Busshe, Syre Johan Grene and Sir Johan Bagot.

And he ordeyned his uncle, Syr Edmond of Langley, Duk of Yorcke, to be his lyeutenaunt whiles he shold be in Irlond in his absence. In this yere deyde the Duc of Lancastre and is buryed at 185 Powlus in London. Thenne Kynge Rychard wente into Irlonde with many lordes and grete ordenaunce; and there he was wel resseyved. And the wilde Irysshmen cam downe to hym with theyr capytaynes and yelded them to hym and swore to be his true lyege men and dyde hym hommage and feawte. Thus he 190 conquerd Irlond the moost part in a lytel whyle.

Whyles Kynge Rychard was in Irlond thus occupyed Syre Harry of Bolyngbrooke, Erle of Derby, the Duc of Lancastres sonne, whome Kynge Rychard hadde made Duk of Herford and had exyled hym for certayn causes, and with hym th'Arche- 195 bisshop of Caunterbury also londed at Ravenspore in the North Contre. And by the coloure of his tytle to the Duchye of Lancastre, he reysed and assembled the people ever as he wente in soo moche as he hadde greete multitude of peple. For the peple were soo oppressyd with the offycers of Kyng Rychard that 200 almoost all the commyns of the londe were redy to awayte on the Erle of Derby hopynge to be relevyd by hym. Incontynent tydynges cam to Kynge Rychard beyng in Irlond how he was landed and that the comons drewe faste to hym. Anone he made 205 hym redy and cam over see into Englond with alle his hooste and arryved in Mylford Haven; and there taryed a two dayes for to refresshe hym and his hooste. And in the mene whyle the lordes and mooste parte of the peple understode that the Erle of Derby bycam strenger and strenger, began to murmure and to grutche. 210 That seynge, Syr Thomas Percy called them togeder, brake the rodde of his offyce, for he was styward, and badde every man goo his wey unwetyng the Kynge. And so in the nyght every man wente his weye levynge the Kynge allone, save two or thre lordes with a fewe men. Whiche lordes for sewerte and by 215 counseyll of the styward brought the Kynge to the castel of Flynt, where he was taken and delyverd to th'Erle of Derby whiche brought hym to London. And thenne were taken at Brystowe Syre William Scrope, Syr Johan Bussh, Sir Harry Grene and Syr Johan Bagot. But Syre Johan Bagot escaped: and 220 the other that were take were byheded. And thus as he was comyng to London warde, tydynges cam to the cyte that Kynge Rycharde was comen to Westmynstre. And anon the peple of London in their furye and wodenesse, as peple maliciously sette ageinst King Richard their soveraine lorde, roose and purposed 225 yf they myght have founden to have destroyed hym. But the mayer and aldermen with the sadde men of the toune with moche werke tourned hem hoome ageyne to London. Yet they toke Syre Johan Slake, Dene of the Kynges Chapel, and putte hym in Ludgate. And Syre Johan Bagot that escaped from Bristowe was 230 take in Irlond and brought to London and sette in Newegate.

Sone after this Kynge Rychard was broughte to the Tour of London. And thenne was ther a parlement in whiche Kynge Rychard was deposed of his crowne and Kynge Henry chosen and taken for the kynge, to whome Kynge Rychard resygned 235 the crowne and the royamme of Englond. And thenne from the Tour he was had to the castel of Ledes in Kente; and from thennes he was had to the castel of Pountfret.

Thenne the Duc of Lancastre, Erle of Derby named Henry Bolyngbroke, was crowned Kyng of Englond at Westmynstre on Saynt Edwardes day Confessour. Thenne made the Kynge his 240 oldest sonne Henry Prynce of Wales, Duke of Cornewayle and Erle of Chestre. He made Syre Thomas of Arondel Archebisshop of Caunterbury, as he was byfore. And he that was made Archebisshop by Kynge Rychard he made hym Bisshop of London. And he made the Erlis sonne of Arondel to be put in possession 245 of all his londes.

In the fyrst yere of his regne he helde his Crystemas at Wyndesore. And on the twelvthe even the Duk of Aumarle tolde the [1399] Kyng how the Duc of Surrey, the Duc of Excetre, the Erle of Salesbury and th'Erle of Gloucetre with other of theyr affynyte 250 were acorded to make a mommynge to the Kyng and soo for to slee hym in the revelynge. Wherfore the Kyng the same nyght cam prively to London. And anon these lordes that had purposed to have made this mommery understode that theyr counseylle was bewrayed, anone with theyr people wente westward. And 255 at Sysseter the Duke of Surrey and the Erle of Salesbury were taken and biheded and their heedes sette on London Brydge. And at Oxenforde were taken two knyghtes, Blount and Sir Benette Sely, and Wyntercele, a squyer, whiche were byheded and quartred and their heedes sette on London Bridge and the 260 quartres sente to other good townes. And at Prithwell in Estsex Sire Johan Holonde, Duck of Excetre, was taken with the comons of the countreye and his heede smyten of and sente to London and sette on London Bridge. Also at Bristowe was take the Lorde Spencer that was made by Kinge Richard Erle of 265 Gloucetre and biheded and his heede sent to London and sette on London Bridge. In the same yere Sire Bernarde Brokeis, Sir John Selley, Syr Johan Mawdelyn and Syr William Ferby were taken and sette in the Tour and after by jugemente were hanged and byheded and theyr heedes sette on London 270 Bridge.

Whanne Kyng Henry sawe that these lordes thus hadde rysen and assemblyd greete peple to have putte hym to deth and for to restore Kynge Rychard ageyne to his crowne and to his royamme,

275 thoughte t'eschue suche peryls; anone commaunded Sir Pyers of Exton that he shold goo strayte to Pountfreyte and delyver the worlde of Kynge Rychard. And soo he departed fro the Kynge and wente to the castel of Pountfret, where as Kynge Rychard was in prysonne, the whiche was sette at table for
280 to dyne. And anone after Syre Pyers cam into the chambre where the Kynge was and eyghte men with hym and eche man an axe in his hond. Trouth it is whan the Kyng sawe Sir Pyers with his felaushippe entre into the chambre defensably arayed, he shoof the table from hym and sprange in the myddes
285 of hem and raughte an axe oute of one of theyr hondes and sette hym self valyauntly at defence. And hym self defendynge he slowe foure of the eyghte. And whanne the sayde Syre Pyers sawe the Kynge soo defende hym, he was soore abasshed and gretely aferde and forthwith sterte upon the place where as Kyng
290 Rychard was wonte to sytte. And as Kynge Rychard foughte and defended hym self goynge bacwarde, the sayd Syre Pyers smote hym on the heede with his axe that he fyll to grounde. Thenne cryed Kynge Rychard: 'God, mercy.' And thenne he gafe hym yet another stroke on the heede and soo he deyde. And thus was
295 thys noble kynge slayne and murthred. And whanne the Kynge was deede, the knyght that hadde thus slayne hym sette hym doune by the deede bodye of Kynge Rychard and byganne to wepe, saynge: 'Alas, what thynge have we doone? We have putte to deth hym that hath ben oure kynge and soverayne lord
300 two and twenty yere. Now have I lost myn honour; ne I shal never come in place but I shal be reproched, for I have done ageynste myn honour.'

After this the twelvest daye of Marche was the bodye of the noble Kyng Rychard broughte thurgh London to Powlus,
305 whiche corps was leyd on a charyotte coveryd with black and foure baners, wherof tweyne were of the armes of Saynt George and tweyne of the armes of Saynt Edward. And there were an honderd men clothed in black, eche berynge a torche; and the cyte of London hadde thyrtty men in whyte, eche berynge also
310 a torche. And the corps was leyd open the vysage that every man myght see and knowe that it was hys body and that he was soo

deede, for many men bylevyd it not. And from thennes he was caryed to the Frerys at Langley and there he was buryed, on whoos sowle God have mercy. Amen.

The comyn oppynyon of Englysshmen is that Kynge Rychard deyde not after the maner aforesayd, but that he deyde other wyse. That is to wete that whanne he herde saye that his brother, the Duc of Excetre, the Duc of Surey, the Erle of Salysbury and the other lordes were deede, he was soo angry and soo sorowfull that he swore that he wolde never eete meete. And soo abode foure dayes withoute etynge, as they saye. And whanne that Kynge Henry understode that he wolde not ete, he sent to hym two prelates for to comforte him. And whan they were come, he confessyd hym to one of them the whiche gaf hym in penaunce that he sholde ete his mete. And whanne he supposed to have eten, the meete myght not goo doune ne avale into his stomake, for the conduytes of his bodye were shronken togeder. And thenne sayde the noble Kynge Rychard that it was done and that he muste nedes deye; and soo he deyde. But certes whether he deyde this waye or that other, certaynly he deyde and was buryed at Langley. God have mercy on his sowle. Amen.

III. The Siege and Conquest of Jerusalem (1481)

The march to Constantinople of the First Crusade

THE yere of th'yncarnacion of Our Lord M fourscore xvj the eght daye of Marche cam a gentilman, a knyght right noble named Gaultier—'without knowleche' to his surname. With hym cam a merveyllous grete plente of folke a foot, for ther were but fewe men a horsbak in this rowte. They passed in Allemayne and drewe hem toward Hongrye. The royamme of Hongrye was alle envyronned with grete waters and large mershes and depe lakes in suche wyse that none myght entre ne yssue but by certayne places and strayt entrees, that ben as yates of the londe. In Hongerye was thenne a Kynge, a moche valyaunt man named

Colemant; and was a very good cristen man. He knewe that Gaultier cam by londe with grete peple and had therof moche grete joye; and helde wel with the pylgremage that he had enterprised. He receyved them debonayrly in his londe and com-
15 manded thurgh his royame that they shold have alle maner vytaylle good cheep[1] and alle that they neded. The pylgryms passed alle Hongrye in good peas tyl they cam to the ende where they founde a water whiche was named Marce. This was the bounde of Hongerye toward th'oryent. They passed this water
20 in good peas and entred into Bongrye. And withoute knowyng of this Gaulteer, some of his peple abode over the water and cam to a castel named Mallevylle for to by vitaylles of the whiche they had nede. The Hongres, bycause that alle the hoost was passed sauf they which were but a fewe, ranne upon them and
25 bette them and dyde to them overmoche shame. They passed the water and cam to Gaultier and shewde to hym playnly how they had ben demened without forfaytte. They had moche grete despite and moche sorowe herof, and had passed the water agayn, yf they had had not so grete peryl and so grete distourblyng; and
30 thought they wold goo theyr waye and leve for t'avenge this thynge.

So long they wente tyl they cam to Bellegrave, whiche is the first cyte of Bongrye on this syde. Gaultier sente to the Duc of the town and requyred hym that he wolde late them ther by vytaylles.
35 He wold not suffre ony to be sold to them. Th'oost had grete disease for lak of vytaylle and myght not lenger kepe them, but that a grete parte of them wente a fowragyng for to gete vytaylles for them and for theyr beestys. They founde grete plente of beestes in the contre, whiche they toke and brought[2] to theyr lodgynges.
40 Whan they of the contre herd this, they armed them and assembled grete peple of the countree and ran upon them where they droef their proyes and fought with them and toke the beestes fro them. And many of them they slewe and hunted the other away. The nombre wel of cxl of oure men shytte them in a
45 monasterye for to kepe them there sauf. But the Bongres cam there aboute and sette fyer on the chirche and brente alle. Gaultier

[1] sheep [2] brougkt

sawe that he ledde with hym many folyssh peple whiche he coude
not rule ne sette alle in ordenaunce; and withdrewe hym fro them
and toke them that wold be ruled and obeye hym and wente into
[the] forestes of Bongrye, which ben large and long, and began 50
to passe the moost wysely and styll that he myght, tyl he cam to
a cyte named Stralyce; and is a contre named Danemarche the
moyen. There fonde he a good man that was Duke of the londe.
Whan this Duke knewe what they were and whyther they wente,
he receyved them moche debonayrly and made them to have 55
vytaylles and other thynges good cheep. And dyde to them
bountes and servyses ynowgh for the oultrage that was doon to
them at Belgrave. And dyde redresse and yelde agayne to them
as moche as he myght recovere and above alle this he delyverd to
them good conduyte and sewr tyl they cam to Constantynoble. 60
Whan they were come to Constantinoble th'Emperour sente for
Gaulteer. He cam unto hym and sayde to hym th'occasion of his
viage and that he wolde abyde there Peter th'eremyte, by the
commandem[en]t of whom he had brought thyse pylgryms.
Whan th'Emperour herde this, he receyved hym moche wel and 65
swetly and assygned to hym a fayr place without the town, where
as he lodged hym with his felawship, and commanded that they
shold have vytaylle and alle other necessaryes good chepe. And
ther sojourned they a whyle.

It was not longe aftir that Peter th'eremite cam fro his contre 70
with grete plente of peple unto the nombre of xl^{m}. He cam into
Lorayne, and passed Francone, Bavyere, Osterych and drewe
hym toward Hungrye. Peter sente his messagers to the Kyng of
Hongrye to th'ende that he myght passe his royamme. He sente
hym worde that he shold have good leve yf they wold goo in 75
peas without medlynges and oultrages. They answerd that they
were pylgryms of Our Lord and had no talente for to trouble the
pees. Thus entred they the royamme of Hongrye and passed by
the lande without ony debate. Vytaylles and other thynges had
they ynough good cheepe. At th'ende they cam to the castel of 80
whiche I spak tofore, named Malevylle. There herd they saye
what was doon to them of the retenue of Gaultier and the grete
oultrage doon to them without cause, and sawe yet the armes and

despoyllis of theyr felaws that had be robbed there hange yet on the walles. Oure pylgryms that sawe this were alle as they had ben out of theyr wytte and ran to armes and began every man to do wel. They toke the toun by force and smote of the heedes of alle them that were within, sauf a fewe which ran into the water and were drowned. Ther were founde of them that were deed wel a four M and of Peters meyne were slayn an C. Whan this was don the hoost fonde there grete plente of vytaylles and abode wel v dayes in that place.

The Duc of Bongrie, which was named Incita, understode how thise pilgryms had venged their felaws ayenst them of Malevylle and doubted for as moche as he had defended the vytaylles to our peple and that he had slayn many of them. And hym semed that Bellegrave was not strong ynough. Therfor he lefte the town and wente into a strenger castel. Thus alle they of the cyte yssued with their goodes and drewe them to the depe forestes. Peter, whyles he laye yet at Malevylle, herd saye that the Kyng of Hongrye had herd of the deth of his peple, wherof he was moche angry, and that he somoned and assembled alle his power for t'avenge his men that had be slayn; and doubted herof, and was no merveylle. Wherfore he made t'assemble alle the shippes that myght be founden atte ryve of the see to hym and made his peple to departe moche hastely, his cartes and charyottes, and the beestes. They had merveyllous grete praye and lad awey grete rychesses fro the castel of Malevylle that they had there taken. Whan they were passed over into Bongrye, they cam tofore Bellegrave and fonde the cyte alle voyde, for they were alle fled.

Aftir they wente eght grete journeyes by many grete forestes tyl they cam tofore a cyte named Nyze. This town fonde they moche stronge and wel wallyd with grete towres and stronge [walles]. And within was grete garnyson and the beste men of warre of alle the londe and grete plente of armours and vytaylle. Peter the heremyte and his hoost fonde a brygge of stone by whiche they passed a water rennyng nyghe to the cyte: they passed the brygge and lodged them bytwene the water and the towne. And bycause they had not mete ynough Peter sente his messages unto the lord of the toun and prayd hym fayr for hym and for his peple that were cristen and pylgryms that wente in the servyse of Our Lord that they myght bye vytaylles of the toun at resonable prys. Thenne the lord sende worde to Peter that he wold not suffre that they shold entre into the toun; but and yf he wold gyve hym good ostages that his peple shold doo no harme 125 ne oultrage to the peple and marcheauntes of the toun that shold come for to selle them vytaylle, he shold sende to them ynough at resonable prys. Whan Peter and his peple herd this they were glad ynough. They delyverd good ostages: and anon they of the town cam out with grete plente of vytayl and other thynges 130 necessarye in the hoost. Moche was this nyght the hoost of the pylgryms refresshyd of alle thynges that they had nede, for they had ben long fro ony good toun. And they of the cyte were to them moche debonair and resonable.

On the morne they demanded theyr ostages and they were 135 delyverd gladly. And forth they wente in peas. But now ye shal here how the devyl doth grete peyne for to empesshe and lette good werkes. In this companye had ben the even afore a stryf to one of the marchauntes[1] of the town and som of the oost. Whan the hoost was departed, the Duchemen assembled to the nombre 140 of an hunderd and for vengeaunce of the stryf. They sawe vij myllenes whiche stode at brygge nyghe the town and sette them a fyre and brente them anone. This was not ynowgh, but there was a litil borough without the cyte and they sette that a fyre also and brende hit to asshes. And syth wente theyr waye aftir 145 theyr felawship whiche knewe nothyng herof. Of this thynge the lord of the town, whiche had the even tofore shewde to them grete debonayrte, was gretely mevyd for he sawe that they rendrid evyl for go[o]d, and was half out of his wytte for angre. This felonnye that this fewe dyde was wyted alle the hoost, whiche 150 was evyl and pyte. He made anon arme alle the town and yssued on horsbak and on fote, hym self cam tofore and prayde and moche desyred his peple for to venge upon thyse false rowters and thevys the oultrage that they had don. Whan they approched the hoost, they fonde fyrst thise thre malefactours whiche had 155 not yet overtaken theyr felaws and ronne on them and smote of

[1] marcchauntes

their heedes. It had thenne be ynowgh; but they were not content, but smote in the aftirst parte of th'oost whiche doubted nothyng. They fonde charyottes, sommyers, mal[ad]es,
160 servauntes, wymmen and childeren,[1] whiche myght not goo so faste as the other. They slewe many and somme they overthrewe and ladde away the cariage. And thus retorned into theyr cyte without hurte and alle blody of the bloode of the pylgryms.

165 Peter was goyng with the grete companye whan a messager cam to hym rydyng and told to hym of this adventure that was fallen in the taylle of th'oost. Peter sente anon to them that were tofore that they shold retourne agayn the way that they were comyn unto the cyte of Nyz. In this retorne they fonde thynges
170 ynowgh that displesyd them, for they fonde their felawes byheded lyeng by the waye. They had grete sorowe herof. One fonde his fader deed, another his brother or his sone, and another his wyf or his doughter. There were many disconvenyents. Peter, whiche had his entencion pure unto Oure Lord, entented not but
175 t'appese the malyce and leye doun the discorde whiche was sourded emong the peple. He sente som wyse and prudent men to the lord and to the moost hye men of the cyte for to demaunde by what occasion they had don this evil and crueltees ayenst the peple of Our Lord. They answerd that this was by the defaulte of
180 the pylgryms and that they had fyrst doon grete oultrage to brenne theyr mylnes and burghe. Whan Peter and the wyse men that were with hym herd this, they thought wel that it was no place ne tyme to venge theyr shames and therfor torned the mater unto peas and acorde for to recouvre the praye, the
185 prysonners and caryage, whiche they had ledde away fro th'oost. For there were of the mene peple whiche wold not be ruled and wold not suffre them of the towne to have pees with us, but wolde avenge by force the oultrage that they had doon. Peter felte this thynge and apperceyved anone the evylle that sourded; and sente
190 of the wysest and grettest of his companye to make the pees. His peple wold not have pees. He made a crye on payne of deth in his name and the name of the barons that no man be so hardy to

[1] childrren

breke the pees that was made. And this he charged upon their pylgremages, theyr feaulte and on th'obedyence that they had promysed hym. And whan they of the hoost herd this, they remevyd not; but folyssh peple wente forth and made grete noyse and wold not obeye. 195

The messagers that were in the town for t'accorde this that was don sawe that the noyse grewe more and more and retourned to theyr felawship[1] withoute ony conclusion or doyng that they had enterprised and dyde theyr best to seece the debate. But they had no power for there were moo than a thousend pylgryms whiche no man myght holde ne reteyne, but that they wold goo armed to the toun. Out of the toun yssued as many or moo ayenst them. Ther began the bataylle and the medle grete and thyk, and began to slee eche other largely. Peter ne his route mevyd not, but byhelde the bataylle. They of the town that were on the walles and at wyndowes sawe that theyr peple had the werse, and apperceyved that the grete power of th'oost entermeted not of this warre and thought that they wold not helpe them, and opened theyr yates and yssued oute by grete rowtes alle armed and smote in the bataylle. And founde of our peple aboute a v^{c} upon the brygge and addressyd to them and slewe them alle, sauf somme that were caste in the water; and alle were perysshed. Whan the grete hoost apperceyved theyr peple thus evyl demened, they myght suffre it no lenger but wente to armes and smote into the bataylle, one aftir another lyke as they myght be armed. The peple that had bygonne this debate were discomfyted fyrst and began to flee so fast that nothyng myght tarye them. They began to bete them an horsbak that cam for to helpe them, by whiche the good men were discomfyted. And they of the cyte that were nygh to theyr retrayt began to chase them moche straytly and to slee them. At last whan oure peple were withdrawen, they retorned by the caryage and harnoys and caryed alle and ledde it with them. And toke wymmen and childeren that myght not flee and putte them in prison. There were wel slayn and lost of the peple of the hoost x^{m}; and the Bongres wan alle the harnoys of th'oost. There was a cart loste that longed to Peter th'eremyte 200 205 210 215 220 225

[1] felawshhip

alle ful of rychesse, whiche had ben yoven to hym in Fraunce for
230 to socoure and sustene the necessytees of the hoost.

They that myght escape fro this discomfiture drewe them into the forestes and hydde them in the depe valeyes in the nyght. And on the morn they began to calle eche other and to whystle and sowne trumpes and busynes in the woodes. And thus began
235 to reassemble and gadred them togydre on a territorie. At the fourth daye were nyghe alle assembled aboute Peter: and they were about a four thousand. They were in moche grete meschyef as they that had lost theyr frendes and theyr peple and almost alle theyr harnoys. Notwithstondyng they lefte not, but wente forth
240 on the waye that they had enterprised with grete mesease and payne for lak of vytaylle. And as they were in this poynt they sawe come ayenst them the messagers of th'Emperour of Constantynoble, whiche spak to Peter. And anon he dyde assemble the heye men and capytayns of the hoost for to here the message that
245 they brought.

And aftir they sayd in this manere. 'Fayr syrs, moche evyl tydynges and renomme is comen of you to our lord, th'Emperour. For it is tolde to hym that ye goo by the countree of his empyre with force and robbe the peple of suche as they have, breke his
250 townes and slee his peple and doo alle the oultrages and wronges that ye may. The good chere, bounte and alle the servyse that is doon to you avaylleth nothyng ne may adoulce ne aswage your hertes. Therfore he commandeth you that ye abyde in none of his cytees more than thre dayes; but goo your waye strayt forth
255 to Constantynoble. For he hath commanded us to goo with you and that we do brynge to you on the waye vytayll good cheep ynowe.'

Whan thise good men herd this that th'Emperour had don to them this bounte, they had grete joye and excused them of thise
260 bataylles and fyghtyng; and shewd openly what the Bongres had doon withoute theyr offence or culpe by force and grete oultrage. The messagers dyrected them on the way tyl they cam to Constantynoble.

IV. Charles the Great (1485)

The joust between Oliver and Fierabras

[The heathen Fierabras challenges Roland or Oliver to fight in single combat against him. Roland refuses; but Oliver, though still wounded from a previous engagement, accepts the challenge so that the Christian faith shall not be without a champion. Seeing Oliver's condition Fierabras offers him a draught of his potion which cures all wounds, but Oliver refuses it.]

AND thys sayd, they lete theyr horses renne wyth a grete courage for to juste at utteraunce. And as they came that one ageynst that other the Frensshemen whych were in their lodgys had grete fere and drede leste it shold mysfalle to Olyver. And emonge al other Charles al wepyng sayd: 'O blessyd Jhesus, I requyre the 5 that at this stroke thou have pyte of Olyver my baron in suche wyse that I may see hym ageyn alyve and in helthe.' And after fervently came into hys chapel hydyng his vysage wyth hys mantel and kneled byfore the crosse and enbraced the crucyfyx wyth grete teeres, sayeng: 'My Lord God, of whome I see here 10 the remembraunce, I byseche the to helpe Olyver, whyche for th'exaltacyon of the crysten fayth is in daunger.'

Thus in contemplacyon of Charles, Fyerabras and Olyver gaf so grete strokes upon theyr sheldes that the hedes of their speres were by force bowed and entred that the fyre sprange out on al 15 sydes and the shaftes of theyr speres were tronchonned that the pyeces flewe in the ayer. The reynes of the brydles of theyr horses wente oute of theyr hondes. Bothe tweyne were so astoned of the stroke and theyr eyen so troubled that in a grete whyle they knewe not on whos syde they were torned. And after that bothe 20 were comen to them self, Fyerabras drewe Plouraunce hys swerde that henge by hys syde and Olyver took Haulteclere mervayllously shynyng and cam upon Fyerabras and on hyghe on hys helme gaf hym so grete a stroke that the floures and precyous stones wherof it was ennobled and garnysshed made to flee to the grounde. And 25 with the same stroke in descendyng he touched hys sholder, but the lether of Capadose saved hym. And the paynym was smyton so harde and sore that bothe hys feet were oute of the styroppes and almoost was overthrowen. Wherof the Frensshemen sayden 30 al wyth one voys: 'A, Saynt Marye, what a stroke hath Olyver gyven to thys paynym.'

'Ye,' sayd Rolland, 'mervaylllously he smote hym. Now wold God of heven', sayd Rolland, 'that I were now under the shelde of my gentyl felowe Olyver, for of me or of the paynym shold 35 shortly be seen the ende.'

To whom the Emperour answerd: 'Ha, evyl gloton, I have wel herde the spoken. Felon coward, it is not now tyme that thou so say, for atte beginnyng thou woldest not goo, wherof many tymes shalt thou be of me reproched.' Upon whych thyng 40 Rolland ansuerd nothyng but that he shold do as it plesed hym.

Fyerabras al astoned of the stroke and replenysshed of grete wrath with his swerd named Plouraunce came wyth a course upon Olyver and gaf hym a stroke[1] upon his helme so sharply that he trenched moo than v^{c} maylles and hurte evyl hys hors and smote 45 of the spore of his foot and a parte of hys thye, wheroute the blode ranne habundantly and the swerde of Fyerabras was al blody. Of whiche stroke Olyver was moeved and troubled that he had fallen ne had hys sadel have been, for he was bowed afterward that he was al tobroken. And his hors began to halte of the 50 stroke. And whan he was comen to hym self wyth an hye voys began to crye: 'O Lord God, my Creatour, O what an evyl stroke have I receyved. O Vyrgyn Marye, Moder of Jhesus, have pyte of me, for overfyersly cutteth the swerde of thys paynym. Yeve me grace that I may ones have hym.' And made upon hym 55 self the sygne of the crosse.

And after Fyerabras sayd to hym: 'Olyver, by Mahoun my god, wyth thys stroke I maad the aferde. Now mayst thou wel fele how I can playe, and I have no mervaylle though thou commaunde the to thy god. But I am evyl contente that I have hurte 60 the oversore with the stroke. Nevertheles be sure that thou shalt not see the sonne goo to reste, for thou begynnest now to chaunge colour and thy fyerce manere. Nevertheles I am contente that thou retorne, and that shall be for the the best tofore thou knowe

[1] stcoke

more fully my strengthe. For I warne the of one thynge that whan I see my blood yssue out of my body, thenne doubleth my myght 65 and my strengthe. And I wote wel that Charles loveth the not moche whan he sendeth the to me. Yf he had lodged the in a fayre bedde and whyte shetes thou haddest been moche better.'

Whan Olyver herde hym so saye he was replenysshed with a fervent courage and began to lyfte up hys heed, and sayd: 'O 70 paynym, dysmesured al day thou vauntest the for to brynge me to th'ende of my dayes. I praye to God Almyghty that he wyl rejoye my courage. Kepe the wel; I deffye the. We have overlong pleted.'

Upon these wordes they ranne togydre, smytyng mervayl- 75 lously eche other upon their helmes in suche wyse that boucles, naylles and crochettes, precious stones, orfaveryes and floures been hewen, broken and flowen to the grounde. The fyre yssued oute largely, makyng grete bruyt with the swerdes upon their harnoys. . . . Al thys whyle perseverd the ij champyons fyghtyng 80 and smytyng eche on other in suche maner that Fyerabras wyth hys swerde brake the cercle of Olyvers helme and made hym falle on hys vysage; and hys hors had be slayn yf he had not lepte asyde. And Olyver was hurte in hys body and specyally in the breste and had thenne loste soo moche of hys blood that he was 85 moche feble, whyche was no merveylle, seen that he had resysted ageynst the moost terryble man that ever was borne of moder.

Olyver, the noble erle, beyng in this malancolye of the grete woundes that he had in hys body took his recomforte sayeng in this manere: '. . . Thus, my God, my Maker, as thys is trouthe 90 and I byleve it verayly and fermly, be ye my[1] comforte ageynst thys myscreaunte that I may vaynquysshe hym in suche wyse that he may be saved.' And this said he blessyd hym with his swerde in makyng the sygne of the crosse in the name of God, the holy Trynyte, and smote his hors upon the hope of the helpe 95 of God.

And Fyerabras sayd to hym lawhyng: 'Olyver, fayre frende, I praye the that thou hyde not fro me the oryson that thou hast said now, for by my god, Termagaunt, I wold gladly here it.'

[1] in (*or* m) my

100 'Now wold God of heven', sayd Olyver, 'that thou were in suche grace that thou sholdest byleve it also fermly as I doo. For I assure the I shold love the thenne as moche as I doo Roulland.'

And Fyerabras ansuerd to hym: 'By my god Mahoun and Termagaunt, thou spekest now of a moche grete folye.' Fyera-105 bras beyng wroth of the wordes of Oliver in grete ire sayd to hym: 'Kepe the wel fro me, for I deffye the.'

'I am redy,' sayd Olyver, 'for to God I commaunde me.'

And so thenne they recountred togyder so sharply and so hard strokes they gaf that the fyre myght haboundantlye be seen 110 sprynge oute of theyr harnoys. Theyr horses bowed under hem and the erthe trembled of the bruyt in the medowe under Mormyonde. Fyerabras took hys swerde in hys honde and smote Olyver there as he was evyl hurt in the breste under the pappe and of that stroke the eyen torned in hys heed and had hys face alle 115 chaunged. And thenne ageyn he cryed on God and on the Virgyn Marie that he wold save his soule.

Fyerabras by grete curtosye sayd to hym: 'Olyver, understonde me. Descende doun surely and goo take of the bawme and drynke at thyn ease, and anone thou shalt be al guarysshed and hole. And 120 thenne mayst thou the better deffende the ageynst me, and thou shalte recovre newe strengthe.' But Olyver for noothynge that he coude do though he shold dye he wold not, for by trewe fightyng he wold have it. And anone came that one ageynst that other and smyten in suche wyse that Fyerabras was hurte daunger-125 ously, for Olyvers swerde entred into his thye an halfe foot depe; and of the blood that yssued oute alle the grasse was reed. And whan he sawe hym so hurte he dranke of hys bawme and was anone al hool, wherof Olyver was moche sorouful bycause therof he coude make none ende of thys paynym. And the 130 Frensshemen that saw this made to God their prayers devoutly that he wolde conserve that day Olyver, and in especyal Charlemayn whiche emong al other loved hym moast entyerly. But whan Olyver sawe the paynym al hole and for the bawme so comforted, by the ayde of God he came to hym and smote hym upon 135 the helme soo harde that the stroke descended upon the sadel and cutte the corde by whyche the barylles were bounden and fastned.

And the hors of Fyerabras was aferde of the stroke and made a lytel course by the playsyr of God. Thenne Olyver, or the paynym toke ony hede, bowed to the grounde and took up the barylles and dranke at hys ease and largely; and anon he was al 140 hole and reconfermed in newe strengthe. And thought that yf by adventure Fyerabras were more hurte by hym and myght ageyn have hys baryllys that in th'ende it myght evyl happe and come to hym. Wherfore he beyng nyghe unto a grete ryver took the barylles and threwe them therin, whyche were anone sonken. 145 And as it is redde, at alle the festes of Saynt Johan these ij barylles ben shewed above the water evydently. Whan Fyerabras sawe that the barilles were loste, allmost for angre he was oute of hys mynde and by grete reproche sayd to Olyver: 'O evyl man that thou arte, thou hast loste my barylles whyche were more worth 150 than al the golde in the world. But I promyse the that or it be even they shal to the ben dere solde, for I shall not cesse tyl I have smyton of thy heed.' And thys sayeng he came ayenst hym. But Olyver, as he that doubteth hym not soo moche as he dyd tofore, eschewed hym not but put hym at the defence wyth his shelde to 155 avoyde the stroke. Nevertheles Fyerabras smote hym so hard that hys helme was desmaylled and broken, but he was not hurte. And the stroke descended so inpytuously that he cutte asondre the necke of Olivers hors; and fyl to grounde. And thenne was Olyver on fote. But a grete myracle it was of the hors of Fyera- 160 bras that maad no semblaunte to renne upon hym as he had ben taught, lyke as I have sayd byfore, but helde hym stylle above hys propre custome. Moche sorouful were the Frensshemen whan they sawe Olyver on fote and wold have armed hem for to socoure hym. But Charles wold not consente for to 165 mayntene hys honour and hys trouthe. And thenne Kyng Charles kneled doun to th'erthe and maad his prayer to God that he wolde comforte Olyver whyche was thus dyspourveyed of his hors.

Whan Olyver sawe hym self on fote he was moche sorouful 170 and came a foure paas nyghe unto Fyerabras and sayd to hym: 'O Kyng of Alexandrye, thou hast borne the foule this day ageynst me. In the mornyng thou hast so moche preysed thy self that thou hast sayd yf v knyghtes came ageynst the, thou woldest abyde and conquere them; and thou knowest that the kyng that sleeth an hors ought to have no parte of th'erytage.'

Fyerabras ansuerd: 'I knowe wel that thou sayest trouthe, but I dyd it not wyth my wylle. Nevertheles to th'ende that thou be not evyl contente wyth me I shal descende doun of my hors and 180 shal gyve to the my hors pomeld; and I promyse the thou shalt be well horsed. And knowe thou that never in my lyf I was so abasshed as whan he sawe the at erthe that he strangled the not, for I never put man to the erthe and thys hors present but that anone he was by hym slayn and dede.'

185 Olyver ansuerd: 'I promyse the that I shal never take thyn hors but yf he be first by me conquered and justly wonne.'

Wherupon Fyerabras was soo moche noble that for the valyaunce of Olyver sayd: 'Certeyn for the noblesse that I knowe in the I wyl do that I never dyd for man.' And sprange of his hors 190 and stode a foote and was contente to fyght ayenst hym a foote bycause he had no hors of hys owne. And the sayd Fyerabras was moche heyer than Olyver. And by one accorde they justed a foote that one ayenst that other so mervayllously that it was wonder that bothe tweyne remayned not in the felde aswoune 195 of the travaylle that they toke. Thus contynueng the bataylle which coude take none ende they spaken many reproches and despyteous wordes that one of theym unto other.

The Kyng Charles seyng al thys had grete pyte on Olyver . . . and after kneled doun with bothe his knees to the grounde and 200 prayed in this manere: 'My Creatour, whyche for our savacyon was borne of the gloryous Vyrgyn Marie in Bethleem, as I wel byleve, that of your glorious byrth al the world was enlumyned, whiche abode in thys world ful xxxij yere and more. And made atte begynnyng Adam and Eve of whom we ben comen and that 205 was in Paradys terrestre, a place moche delectable. And there by you were alle fruytes abandoned to them except one onely, whyche was of knowyng good and evyl, as it plesed you to ordeyne. Of whiche Adam ete and was dysobeysaunt. For whom to the reparacion of his misdede and for to redeme hym fro 210 eternal captyvyte and us also, ye were contente to take the deth in the tree of the crosse after that the traytour[1] Judas solde you for xxx pens. And on a Friday ye were payned and your handes and feet mortally naylled and crowned with a moche sharpe crowne of thornes. And after Longyus smote you in the ryght syde to the hert, whiche was blynde. And after that he had leyed on hys eyen 215 of your precyous blood he sawe moche clerely. And after ye descended into helle and toke oute your frendes and sythe aroos fro deth to lyf. And tofore al your apostles ye ascended into heven and lefte for your lyeutenaunt Saynt Peter th'appostle in erthe. And ordeynest baptesme for the regeneracyon of us and to make 220 us crysten for to have salvacyon. O Lord, as alle thys is truthe and that I byleve it stedfastly, so on thys day be thou in ayde and socour unto Olyver for to preserve hym that he be not slayn ne vaynquysshed.'

He thys sayeng and other devoute wordes in hys secrete 225 oratorye Our[2] Lord sente to hym an aungel fro heven whyche sayd to hym: 'O Charles, emperour of noblesse, knowe thou for trouthe that I am sente from God for to say to the that thou doubte nothynge of Olyver, for wythout faylle he shal wynne the bataylle, though it be late; but he shal vaynquysshe the 230 paynym.' Thys sayd, the aungel departed and Charles thanked God devoutelye for hys gloryous medytacyon.

Nevertheles after many bataylles bytwene Fyerabras and Olyver maad and grete menaces, [Fyerabras] by grete furour wyllyng to have gyven to Olyver a grete stroke oute of mesure. 235 But Olyver whyche sawe the stroke comyng devaunced hym in suche wyse that he gaf two evyl strokes to Fyerabras, wherof Fyerabras was passyng angry upon Olyver and Olyver on hym so that bothe were ryght actyf never to departe tyl that one of them were vaynquysshed and destroyed. And at that tyme 240 Olyver was soo coveytous in smytyng that his honde in whiche he helde hys swerde was aslepe and swollen for the payne that he had of smytyng, and he desyryng to smyte hys enemye at utteraunce hys suerde flewe aferre fro hym out of his hande, wherof he was sore moeved and abasshed; and it was no mer- 245 vaylle. And moche courageously ranne for to take up his swerde

[1] traycour [2] Out

and layed hys shelde on hys hede for to preserve it. But notwythstondyng the paynym smote hym twyes so myghtyly that he brake hys shelde in dyvers places and hys hauberke so that he was
250 sore astonyed for that tyme and doubted soo moche the paynym that he durst not take hys swerde. And moche sodeynlye the Frensshemen, which sawe so Olyver dyspourveyed of his swerde, armed them anone and were in purpoos to renne upon the Sarasyn for to socour Olyver. But Charles wold not consente
255 that ony man shold goo, sayeng to them that God is almyghty for to save and mayntene hym in hys good ryght. For yf he had not gaynsayed it, more than xiiij thousand men were thenne redy for to have rescowed hym.

And notwythstondyng al thys the paynym dyd but laughe and
260 said to Olyver: 'In trouthe, Olyver, I have opteyned upon the a lytel of myn entente. But wherfore darst not thou take thy swerde? I knowe now wel that thou art ynough vaynquysshed sythe that thou art so aferde that thou darst not stoupe for all the tresour of the world. And I am wel contente for to apoynte wyth
265 the, that is that thou renye the fayth that thou holdest, the baptesme that thou hast receyved and the god in whom thou bylevest and for whome thou hast had al thys payne, and byleve in Mahoun, my god, ful of bounte, and I shal suffre the to lyve. And moreover I shal be contente to gyve to the my sister to wyf
270 to whom thou shalte be rychely maryed. Hyr name is Florypes, the fayrest of moder borne. And after we shal conquere Fraunce or thys yere be paste; and of one of the royames I shal crowne the kyng.'

Olyver ansuerd to hym: 'Paynym, thou spekest to me of grete
275 folye, for God forbede that ever I shold be of entencion to forsake my god, whyche hath created and fourmed me, and his holy sacrements, which have been establysshed for my savacyon, for to byleve in Mahoun and in thy goddes ful of abusyon, whiche have neyther strengthe ne vertue but cause of dampnacyon.'

280 Fyerabras sayd to hym: 'By Mahoun, my god, thou art alwaye moche obstynat that ne for payn ne for torment thou wylt not denye thy fayth. And of one thynge which is more grete thou mayst wel avaunte the, for never was I of persone so travailled ne

greved as I am of the. Thou oughtest wel to be praysed. I am contente that thou take thy swerde hardyly and surely, for with- 285 oute competent wepen thou mayst not prevaylle ne more than a woman.'

Olyver answerd: 'Paynym, I can not say the contrarye but that thou offrest to me servyce and bounte, but for the valewe of x thousand marke of golde I wyl not take it, ne for to deye ther- 290 fore. For yf I had recoverd my swerde by thy curtosye and it happed that thou were under my puyssaunce and thou thenne demaundest of me amytye and frendshyp and thenne [I] put the to deth, it shold to me be vylete and reproche. And at thys tyme my lyf and my deth be in the wylle of God to whom I have gyven 295 my self over. But and yf I may wynne my swerde, thou shalt bye it dere and here deye, for other thynge shal thou not have.'

'By my fayth,' sayd Fyerabras, 'thou art moche surquydrous and gloryous. Wherfore be thou sure that shortely thou shalt be confused, descomfyte and matte.' 300

Whan Fyerabras herde that Oliver was so fyers of fayt and of courage, he had grete mervaylle, for he wold not have hys swerde but yf he myght by juste warre conquere it. Wherfore the paynym dysmesurably came ageynst hym and helde in hys hande Plorance hys swerde. Thenne it was no mervayle though 305 Olyver was aferde to abyde hys enemye, he beyng dyspourveyed of swerde and of shelde, for that was broken in two partyes. But as it playsed to God he loked besyde hym and sawe the hors of Fyerabras and on the arson of the sadel were ij other swerdes of whych I have spoken afore. And anone Olyver ranne ryght 310 quyckely and took one of the swerdes whych was named Baptesme, whyche had the blade moche large and shone mervayllously, and after came ageynst the paynym and put tofore parte of hys shelde suche as was lefte. And whan he was nyghe hym he began to say: 'O Kyng of Alexandrye, now is tyme to compte, 315 for I am pourveyed of your swerde of whych I shal make you wroth. And kepe you wel from me for I have deffyed you.'

Thenne whan Fyerabras sawe it and had herde hym so speke, anone began to chaunge colour and sayd: 'O Baptym, good swerde, I have kepte the many a day for one of the beste that ever 320

henge by my syde or by ony mans that is lyvyng.' And after behelde Olyver sayeng: 'By my god Mahoun, I knowe the a man of grete fyerste. I wold that thou woldest take thyn owne swerde and late me have myn and thenne late us fyght as we have
325 begonne.'

'By my hede,' sayd Olyver, 'that shal never be by my wylle, for tofore I make ony pacte with the I shal assaye and approve thys swerde upon thy persone. Kepe the wel fro me for overlong have we sermoned.'

330 Thys sayeng and other thynges Olyver came as a lyon hungry ayenst Fyerabras and smote hym fyrst. But he myght not attayne hym on the hede but that he recountred first the shelde of the paynym, whyche he brake and al tofrusshed evyl that the half flewe in the felde. Thenne Fyerabras was sore aferde of that stroke
335 for above alle thys the swerde wyth that stroke entred nygh half a foot within th'erthe. Thenne Olyver blessyd hym that had forged that swerde and so wel tempred. And after many menaces rygorous they were in partye descouverd of theyr helmes. And whan Olyver sawe the paynym Fyerabras in the vysage fyers and
340 courageous, he sayd: 'O Lord God of heven, Maker of heven and of erthe, that thys paynym is noble and ful of cruelte. Now wold God that Charles had hym in his power and yf he wold be baptysed, Rolland and I shold be hys pryve felowes. O glorious Vyrgyn Marie, moder of God, praye Our Lord Jhesu Cryste, thy
345 sone, that he gyve grace to thys Sarasyn that he may byleve in the cristen fayth, for by hym it may be moche enhaunced.'

Fyerabras ansuerd in thys manere: 'Olyver, leve suche wordes. Telle me yf thou wylt fyght like as thou hast enterprysed.'

'Ye,' sayd Olyver, 'kepe the wel fro me for I deffye the'; and
350 ranne upon hym. And Olyver was smyton fyrst upon his shelde by suche fiersnes that he smote his shelde in pyeces nyghe to hys fyste, and it was mervaylle that he cut it not of. Wherfore Fyerabras sayd that he had put hym in suche caas that he shold not longe lyve in thys world. Olyver sayd noo worde but came with his
355 swerde ayenst the paynym Fyerabras moche furyously. Thenne the paynym that sawe the stroke come threwe hys shelde ayenst Olyver, wherfore anone it was quartred, and was so astoned that

the eyen in his heed were al troubled of the payne, and the fyre was seen sprynge oute of the swerdes and sheldes moche habundantlye. 360

And thus in smytyng Fyerabras sayd in this manere: 'Now is the houre come that thou shalt never have ayde of thy god Jhesus in whome thou bylevest that anone thou shalt be deed sythe thou felest thy self overcomen.'

And Olyver anone ansuerd: 'Jhesus is wel myghty for to shewe 365 hys puyssaunce. But anone thou shalt knowe that Mahoun ne Termagaunte shal not mowe ayde the ne be so myghty but that thou shalte be deed. I shal wel gyve the knowleche.'

And herupon came that one upon that other. And Olyver was smyton on the helm al unto the flesshe in suche wyse that al that the 370 swerde araught it share and passed thorugh. And thenne he sayd to Olyver: 'I suere to the by my god that I have wel araught the and smyton. Never shal Charles ne Rolland see the, be thou wel sure.'

Olyver ansuerd: 'O Fyerabras of Alexandrye, be not thou so proude for or I departe fro the I shal rendre the dede or vayn- 375 quysshed. And God graunte to me that whyche I have alwaye desyred.'

And therupon eche smote other so merveyllously that the bodyes of them bothe swette for anguysshe and payne. Fyerabras smote Olyver upon the helme soo harde that the stroke came to 380 the flessh, and yf God had not wrought he had be slayn at that tyme. Wherfore Olyver as a man enraged came ayenst the paynym. And the Sarasyn lyfte on hyghe hys shelde so that he was al dyscoverd under the arme and hys flanke was there unarmed. Olyver was wyse and took good hede and came lyghtly 385 and smote Fyerabras in hys flanke so myghtyly and contynued in suche wyse that he thrested his swerde in one of hys flankes wel depe. And hys swerde, hym self and the place was alle bybled of the blood. Thus was Fyerabras hurte in suche manere that almoost hys bowellys yssued oute of his bely, for thenne at that 390 stroke Olyver employed al his strengthe for to make an ende of the bataylle so longe foughten.

After that the paynym was smyton and hurte mortally as I have sayd and he seyng that he myght no more resyste ayenst

395 Olyver, by the vertu of God he was enlumyned in suche wyse that he had knowleche of the errour of the paynyms and lyfte up hys eyen unto heven and began to escrye the holy Trynyte and the grace of the Holy Ghoost. And after loked on Olyver and sayd to hym: 'O noble Olyver, and valyaunt knyght, in th'onour 400 of God on whome thou bylevest and to whome I consente, I crye the mercy and requyre the that I dye not tyl I be baptysed and yelden vaynquysshed unto Charles the Emperour, whyche so moche is redoubted. For I shal byleve in the crysten fayth and shal yelde the relyques for whyche ye be assemblyd and have 405 taken soo moche payne. And I swere to the that yf by thy defaute I dye Sarasyn, I make the culpable of my dampnacyon. And yf thou take not me into thy garde I shal lose my blood; thou shalt see me deye tofore thyn eyen. Wherfore in the honour of God have pyte on me.'

V. **Reynard the Fox** (1481)

The duel between Reynard and Isegrim

[After various escapades Reynard is brought to the court of Noble the lion to answer the charges raised against him, principally by Isegrim the wolf. Reynard tries to extricate himself by subtle lying, but eventually Isegrim challenges him to defend himself against the charge of treachery in a trial by combat. In preparation for the duel Reynard cuts off all his hair and oils his skin to make it slippery. He also holds his water overnight so that he can urinate plentifully into his tail. Having made their preparations, the two combatants enter the lists.]

THE foxe said not one worde, but kneled doun lowe to th'erthe unto the Kynge and to the Quene and stryked hym forth into the felde. The wulf was ther redy and spack many a proud word. The rulers and kepars of the felde was the lupaert and the losse. 5 They brought forth the booke on whiche sware the wulf that the foxe was a traytour and a morderar and none myght be falser than he was, and that he wolde preve on his body and make it good. Reynart the foxe sware that he lyed as a false knave and a cursyd theef and that he wold doo good on his body. Whan this was don the governours of the felde bad them doo theyr devoyr. 10 Thenne romed they alle the felde sauf Dame Rukenawe the she-ape. She abode by the foxe and bad hym remembre wel the wordes that she had sayd to hym. She said: 'See wel too. Whan ye were vij yer olde ye were wyse ynowh to goo by nyght wythout lanterne or moneshyne where ye wyste to wynne ony 15 goode. Ye ben named emong the peple wyse and subtyl. Payne your self to werke soo that ye wynne the prys. Thenne may ye have ever honour and worship and al we that ben your frendys.'

He answerd: 'My derest aunte, I knowe it wel. I shal doo my beste and thynke on your counseyl. I hope so to doo that alle my 20 lignage shal have worship therby and myn enemyes shame and confusion.'

She sayde: 'God graunte it yow.'

Therwyth she wente out of the felde and lete them tweyne goo togydre. The wulf trade forth to the foxe in grete wrath and 25 opened his forefeet[1] and supposed to have taken the foxe in hem. But the foxe sprang fro hym lyghtly, for he was lyghter to fote than he. The wulf sprange after and hunted the foxe sore. Theyr frendes stode without the lystes and loked upon hem. The wulf strode wyder than Reynard dyde and ofte overtoke hym and 30 lyfte up his foot and wende to have smyten hym. But the foxe sawe to and smote hym wyth his rowhe tayle, whiche he had al bepyssed, in his visage. Tho wende the wulf to have ben plat blynde. The pysse sterte in his eyen. Thenne muste he reste for to make clene[2] his eyen. Reyner thougthe on his fordele and stode 35 above the wynde skrabbing and casting wyth his feet the duste that it flewe the wulfis eyen ful. The wulf was sore blynded therwyth in suche wyse that he muste leve the rennyng after hym, for the sonde and pysse clevyd under his eyen that it smerted so sore that he must rubbe and wasshe it away. 40

Tho cam Reyner in a grete angre and bote hym thre grete woundes on his heed wyth his teeth and said: 'What is that, Syr Wulf? Hath one there byten yow? How is it wyth yow? I wyl al otherwyse on yow yet. Abyde, I shal brynge yow somm newe

[1] sore feet [2] elene

45 thyng. Ye have stole many a lambe and destroyed many a symple beest, and now falsely have appeled me and brought me in this trouble. Al this shal I now avenge on the. I am chosen to reward the for thyn old synnes, for God[1] wyl no lenger suffre the in thy grete ravayn and shrewdnes. I shal now assoylle the and that shal 50 be good for thy sowle. Take paciently this penaunce for thou shalt lyve no lenger. The helle shal be thy purgatorye. Thy lyf is now in my mercy. But and yf thou wilt knele doun and aske me forgyfnes and knowleche the to be overcomen, yet though thou be evyl, yet I wyl spare the for my conscience counseylleth me I 55 shold not gladly slee no man.'

Isegrym wende wyth thyse mockyng and spytous wordes to have goon out of his wytte. And that dered hym so moche that he wyste not what to saye buff ne baff, he was so angry in his herte. The woundes that Reynart had gyven hym bledde and 60 smerted sore. And he thought how he myghte best avenge it. Wyth grete angre he lyft up his foot and smote the foxe on the heed so grete a stroke that he fyl to the ground. Tho sterte the wulf to and wende to have take hym. But the foxe was lyght and wyly and roose lyghtly up and mette wyth hym fiersly. And there 65 began a felle bataylle whiche dured longe. The wulf had grete spyte on the foxe as it wel semed. He sprange after hym x tymes eche after other and wold fayn have had hym faste. But his skyn was so slyper and fatte of the oyle that alway he escaped fro hym. O so subtyl and snelle was the foxe that many tymes whan the 70 wulf wende wel to be sure of hym, he sterte thenne bytwene his legges and under his bely and thenne torned he agayn and gaf the wulf a stroke wyth his tail ful of pysse in his eyen that Isegrym wende he sholde have loste his sight. And this dyde he often tymes. And alwey whan he had so smyten hym, thenne wold he 75 goo above the wynde and reyse the duste that it made his eyen ful of stufs. Isegrym was woo begon and thought he was at an afterdele. Yet was his strengthe and myght moche more than the foxes. Reynard had many a sore stroke of hym whan he raught hym. They gaf eche other many a stroke and many a byte whan 80 they saw theyr avauntage; and eche of hem dyde his best to

[1] good

destroye that other. I wold I myght see suche a bataylle: that one was wyly and that other was stronge; that one faught wyth strengthe and that other with subtylte.

The wulf was angry that the foxe endured so longe ayenst hym. Yf his formest feet had ben hole the foxe had not endured so 85 longe, but the sores were so open that he myght not wel renne. And the foxe myght better of and on than he; and also he swange his tayl wyth pysse ofte under his eyen and made hym that hym thougthe that his eyen shold goo out.

Atte laste he sayd to hym self: 'I wyl make an ende of this 90 bataylle. How longe shal this caytyf dure thus ayenst me? I am so grete I shold, yf I laye upon hym, presse hym to deth. Hit is to me a grete shame that I spare hym so longe. Men shal mocke and poynte me wyth fyngres to my shame and rebuke for I am yet on the werst syde. I am sore wounded; I blede sore; and he drowneth 95 me wyth his pysse and caste so moche dust and sande in myne eyen that hastely I shal not conne see yf I suffre hym ony lenger. I wyl sette it in aventure and seen what shal come therof.'

Wyth that he smote wyth his foot Reynard on the heed that he fyll doun to the ground. And er he cowde aryse he caught hym 100 in his feet and laye upon hym, as he wold have pressed hym to deth. Tho began the foxe to be aferd and so were alle his frendis whan they sawe hym lye under. And on that other syde alle Ysegryms frendes were joyeful and glad. The foxe defended hym faste wyth his clawes as he laye upward wyth his feet and gaf 105 hym many a clope. The wulf durste not wyth his feet doo hym moche harme, but wyth his teeth snatched at hym as he wold have byten hym. Whan the foxe sawe that he shold be byten and was in grete drede, he smote the wulf in the heed wyth his formest clawes and tare the skynne of bytwene his browes and hys 110 eeris and that one of his eyen henge out, whiche dyde hym moche payne. He howlyd; he wepte; he cryde lowde and made a pyteuous noyse for the blode rann doun as it had ben a streme. The wulf wyped his eyen. The foxe was glad whan he sawe that. He wrastled so sore that he sprang on his feet whyles he rubbed 115 his eyen. The wulf was not wel plesyd therwythalle and smote after hym er he escaped and caught hym in his armes and helde

hym faste, notwythstandyng that he bledde. Reynard was woo thenne. There wrastled they longe and sore. The wulf wexe so
120 angry that he forgat al his smarte and payne and threw the foxe al plat under hym, whiche cam hym evyl to passe for his one hand by whiche he deffended hym sterte in the fallyng into Ysegryms throte—and thenne was he aferd to lese his hand.

The wulf sayd tho to the foxe: 'Now chese whether ye wyl
125 yelde yow as overcome or ellis I shal certaynly slee yow. The skateryng of the dust, thy pysse, thy mockyng ne thy deffence ne alle thy false wylys may not now helpe the. Thou mayste not escape me. Thou hast heretofore don me so moche harme and shame, and now I have lost myne one eye and therto sore
130 wounded.'[1]

Whan Reynard herde that it stode so rowme: that he shold chese to knowleche hym overcomen and yelde hym or ellis to take the deth, he thought the choys was worth ten marke, and that he muste saye that one or that other. He had anon concluded
135 what he wold saie and began to saye to hym wyth fayr wordes in this wyse. 'Dere eme, I wyl gladly become your man wyth alle my good. And I wyl goo for you to the holy grave and shal gete pardon and wynnyng for your cloistre of alle the chyrches that ben in the holy lande, whiche shal moche prouffyte to your sowle and
140 your elders sowles also. I trowe ther was never suche a prouffre prouffred to ony kynge. And I shal serve you lyke as I shold serve our holy fader, the Pope. I shal holde of you al that I have and ever ben your servaunt and forth I shal make that al my lignage shal do in lyke wyse. Thenne shal ye be a lord above alle
145 lordes. Who shold thenne dare doo onythyng ayenst you? And furthermore what somever I take of polaylle, ghees, partrych or plovyer, fysshe or flesshe or what somever it be, therof shal ye fyrst have the choys and your wyf and your chyldren er ony come in my body. Therto I wyl alway abyde by you that where ye be
150 ther shal no hurte ne scathe come to yow. Ye be strong and I am wyly. Late us abyde togydre, that one wyth the counseyl and that other wyth the dede, then may ther nothyng mysfalle to us ward. And we ben so nygh of kynne eche to other that of right

[1] woundeed

shold be no angre bytwene us. I wold not have foughten ayenst you yf I myght have escaped. But ye appeled me fyrst unto 155 fyghte. Tho muste I doo that I not doo wold gladly. And in this bataylle I have ben curtoys to yow. I have not yet shewde the utterist of my myght on yow lyke as I wold have doon yf ye had ben a straunger to me. For the nevew ought to spare the eme: it is good reson and it ought so to bee. Dere eme, so have I now 160 doo. And that maye ye marke wel whan I ran tofore yow: myn herte wold not consente therto. For I myght have hurte yow moche more than I dyde, but I thought it never. For I have not hurte yow ne don yow so moche harm that may hyndre yow sauf only that myshappe that is fallen on your eye. Ach! therfore[1] 165 I am sory and suffre moche sorow in my herte. I wold wel, dere eme, that it had not happed yow, but that it had fallen on me, so that ye therwyth had ben plesyd, how be it that ye shal have therby a grete avauntage for whan ye hereafter shal slepe ye nede not to shette but one wyndowe, where another muste shette two. 170 My wyf and my children and my lignage shal falle dounn to your feet tofore the Kynge and tofore alle them that ye wyl desyre and praye yow humbly that ye wyl suffre Reynart your nevew lyve. And also I shal knoweleche ofte to have trespaced ayenst yow and what lesynges I have lyed upon yow. How 175 myght ony lord have more honour than I proffre yow? I wold for no good do this to another; therfore I pray yow to be plesyd herewythal. I wote wel, yf ye wolde, ye myght now slee me. But and ye so don had, what had ye wonne? So muste ye ever after this tyme kepe yow fro my frendes and lignage. Therfore 180 he is wyse that can in his angre mesure hym self and not be overhasty and to see wel what may falle or happe afterward to hym. What man that in his angre can wel advyse hym, certaynly he is wyse. Men fynde many fooles that in hete hasten hem so moche that after they repente hem and thenne it is[2] to late. But, dere eme, 185 I trowe that ye be to wyse so to doo. Hit is better to have prys, honour, reste and pees and many frendes that be redy to helpe hym than to have shame, hurte, unreste and also many enemyes lyeng in a wayte to doo hym harme. Also it is lityl worship to

[1] thersore [2] this

190 hym that hath overcomen a man thenne to slee hym; it is grete shame; not for my lyf, thaugh I were deed that were a lytyll hurte.'

Isegrym the wulf said: 'Ay, theef, how fayn woldest thow be losed and dyscharged fro me, that here I wel by thy wordes. 195 Were thou now fro me on thy free feet, thou woldest not sette by me an eggeshelle. Though thou promysedest to me alle the world of fyn rede gold I wold not late the escape. I sette lytyl by the and alle thy frendes and lignage. Alle that thou hast here said is but lesyngis and fayned falsenes. Wenest thou thus to 200 deceyve me? It is longe syth that I knewe the. I am no byrde to be locked ne take by chaf. I know wel ynowh good corn. O, how woldest thou mocke me yf I lete the thus escape. Thou myghtest wel have said this to one that knewe the not, but to me thou losest thy flateryng and swete floytyng for I understande to wel 205 thy subtyl, lyeng talys. Thow hast so ofte deceyved me that me behoveth now to take good hede of the. Thow false stynkyng knave, thow saist that thou hast spared me in this batayl. Loke hetherward to me. Is not myn one eye out? And therto hast thou wounded me in xx places in my heed. Thou woldest not suffre 210 me so longe to reste as to take ones my breeth. I were overmoche a fool yf I shold now spare the or be mercyful to the, so many a confusion and shame as thou hast don to me; and that also that toucheth me most of alle that thou hast disworshiped and sklaundred Erswyn my wyf, whom I love as wel as my self, and 215 falsely fors[ed]est and deceyvedest her, whiche shal never out of my herte, for as ofte as it cometh to myn mynde alle myn angre and hate that I have to the reneweth.'

In the mene wylle that Ysegrym was thus spekyng, the foxe bithought hym how he myght helpe hym self. And stack his 220 other hond after bytwene his legges and grepe the wulf fast by the colyons, and he wronge hem so sore that for woo and payne he muste crye lowde and howle. Thenne the foxe drewe his other hond out of his mouth. The wulf had so moche payne and anguyssh of the sore wryngyng that the foxe dowed and wronge 225 his genytours that he spytte blood, and for grete payne he byshote hym self. This payne dyde hym more sorow and woo than his eye dyde that so sore bledde. And also it made hym to overthrowe alle in a swowne for he had so moche bledde, and also the threstyng that he suffred in his colyons made hym so faynt that he had lost his myght. Thenne Reynard the foxe lepe upon hym wyth al his myght and caught hym by the legges and drewe hym forth thurgh the felde that they alle myght see it. And he stack and smote hym sore. Thenne were Ysegryms frendes al ful of sorowe and wente al wepyng unto theyr lord the Kynge and prayde hym that he wold doo sece the batayll and take it up into his handes. The Kynge graunted it. 230 235

And thenne wente the kepars of the felde, the lupaerd and the lossem, and saide to the foxe and to the wulf: 'Our lord the Kynge wil speke wyth yow and wyl that this batayl be ended. He wil take it into his hand. He desyreth that ye wyl gyve your stryf unto hym, for yf ony of yow here were slayn it shold be grete shame on bothe sydes, for ye have as moche worship of this felde as ye may have.' And they sayde to the foxe: 'Alle the beestis gyve to yow the prys that have seen this bataylle.' 240

The foxe said: 'Therof I thanke hem. And what that shal plese my lord to commande that shal not I gaynsaye. I desire no better but to have wonne the felde.' 245

VI. **Le Morte d'Arthur:** Book Five (1485)

The start of Arthur's campaign against Lucius

[Messengers from the Emperor of Rome demand tribute from England and claim that Arthur owes allegiance to the Empire. Arthur rejects this claim and announces that he will go to the Continent to reconquer England's rightful possessions. The Emperor Lucius makes his preparations for the struggle.]

NOW leve we of Lucius the Emperour and speke we of Kynge Arthur that commaunded alle them of his retenue to be redy atte utas of Hyllary for to holde a parlement at Yorke. And at that parlement was concluded to areste alle the navye of the lond and to be redy within xv dayes at Sandwyche. And there he shewed 5

to his armye how he purposed to conquere th'empyre whiche he ought to have of ryght; and there he ordeyned two governours of this royame, that is to say Syre Bawdewyn of Bretayne for to counceille to the best and Syr Constantyn, sone to Syre Cador of
10 Cornewaylle, whiche after the dethe of Arthur was kyng of this royamme. And in the presence of alle his lordes he resyned the rule of the royame and Gwenever his quene to them; wherfore Syre Launcelot was wrothe for he lefte Syre Trystram with Kynge Marke for the love of beal Isoulde. Thenne the Quene
15 Gwenever made grete sorowe for the departynge of her lord and other, and swouned in suche wyse that the ladyes bare her into her chambre.

Thus the Kyng with his grete armye departed levyng the Quene and royamme in the governaunce of Syre Bawduyn and Con-
20 stantyn. And whan he was on his hors he sayd with an hyhe voys: 'Yf I dye in this journey I wyl that Syre Constantyn be myn heyer and kyng crowned of this royame as next of my blood.' And after departed and entred into the see atte Sandwyche with alle his armye with a greete multitude of shyppes, galeyes, cogges
25 and dromoundes sayllynge on the see.

And as the Kyng laye in his caban in the shyp he fyll in a slomerynge and dremed a merveyllous dreme. Hym semed that a dredeful dragon dyd drowne moche of his peple, and he cam fleynge oute of the west. And his hede was enameled with asure
30 and his sholders shone as gold, his bely lyke maylles of a merveyllous hewe, his taylle ful of tatters, his feet ful of fyne sable and his clawes lyke fyne gold; and an hydous flamme of fyre flewe oute of his mouthe lyke as the londe and water had flammed all of fyre. After hym semed there came oute of th'oryent a grymly
35 bore, al blak, in a clowde and his pawes as bygge as a post; he was rugged, lokynge roughly; he was the foulest beest that ever man sawe; he rored and romed soo hydously that it were merveill to here. Thenne the dredeful dragon avaunced hym and cam in the wynde lyke a fawcon gyvynge grete strokes on the bore. And
40 the bore hytte hym ageyne with his grysly tuskes that his brest was al blody and that the hote blood made alle the see reed of his blood. Thenne the dragon flewe awey al on an heyghte and

came doune with suche a swough and smote the bore on the rydge, whiche was x foote large fro the hede to the taylle, and smote the bore all to powdre bothe flesshe and bonys that it 45 flytteryd al abrode on the see.

And therwith the Kynge awoke anone and was sore abasshed of this dreme, and sente anone for a wyse philosopher commaundynge to telle hym the sygnyfycacion of his dreme.

'Syre,' sayd the philosopher, 'the dragon that thow dremedest 50 of betokeneth thyn owne persone that sayllest here and the colours of his wynges ben thy royames that thow haste wonne, and his taylle whiche is al totatterd sygnefyeth the noble knyghtes of the Round Table. And the bore, that the dragon slough, comyng fro the clowdes betokeneth some tyraunt that tor- 55 menteth the peple, or els thow arte lyke to fyghte with somme geaunt, thy self, beynge horryble and abhomynable whoos pere ye sawe never in your dayes. Wherfore of this dredeful dreme doubte the nothynge but as a conquerour comeforth thy self.'

Thenne after this soone they had syghte of londe and saylled 60 tyl they arryved atte Barflete in Flaundres. And whanne they were there he fond many of his grete lordes redy as they had ben commaunded to awayte upon hym.

Thenne came to hym an husbondman of the countrey and told hym how there was in the countre of Constantyn besyde 65 Bretayne a grete gyaunt whiche hadde slayne, murthered and devoured moche peple of the countreye; and had ben susteyned seven yere with the children of the comyns of that land in soo moche that alle the children ben alle slayne and destroyed. 'And now late he hath taken the Duchesse of Bretayne as she rode with 70 her meyne and hath ledde her to his lodgynge, whiche is in a montayne, for to ravysshe and lye by her to her lyves ende. And many people folowed her, moo than v^{c}, but alle they myghte not rescowe her; but they lefte her shrykyng and cryenge lamentably. Wherfore I suppose that he hath slayn her in fulfyllynge 75 his fowle lust of lechery. She was wyf unto thy cosyn, Syre Howel, whome we calle ful nyhe of thy blood. Now as thow [arte] a ryghtful kynge have pyte on this lady, and revenge us al as thow arte a noble conquerour.'

80 'Alas,' sayd Kynge Arthur, 'this is a grete meschyef. I had lever than the best royame that I have that I hadde ben a forlonge way tofore hym for to have rescowed that lady. Now, felawe,' sayd Kynge Arthur, 'canst thou brynge me there as thys gyaunt haunteth?'

85 'Ye, syre,' sayd the good man, 'loo yonder where as thow seest tho two grete fyres, there shalt thou fynde hym and more tresour than I suppose is in al Fraunce.'

Whanne the Kynge hadde understanden this pyteous caas he retorned into his tente. Thenne he callyd to hym Syre Kaye and 90 Syre Bedewere and commaunded them secretely to make redy hors and harneis for hym self and them tweyne. For after evensonge he wold ryde on pylgremage with them two only unto Saynt Mychels Mounte. And thenne anone he maad hym redy and armed hym at alle poyntes and tooke his hors and his sheld. 95 And soo they thre departed thens and rode forthe as faste as ever they myght tyl that they cam to the forlond of that mount. And there they alyghted and the Kynge commaunded them to tarye there for he wold hym self goo up into that mounte.

And soo he ascended up into that hylle tyl he came to 100 a grete fyre and there he fonde a careful wydowe wryngynge her handes and makyng grete sorowe, syttynge by a grave newe made. And thenne Kynge Arthur salewed her and demaunded of her wherfore she made suche lamentacion.

To whome she ansuerd and sayd: 'Syre knyghte, speke softe for 105 yonder is a devyll. Yf he here the speke he wylle come and destroye the. I hold the unhappy. What dost thow here in this mountayne? For yf ye were suche fyfty as ye be, ye were not able to make resystence ageynst this devyl. Here lyeth a duchesse deede, the whiche was the fayrest of alle the world, wyf to Syre 110 Howel Duc of Bretayne. He hath murthred her in forcynge her and hath slytte her unto the navyl.'

'Dame,' sayd the Kynge, 'I come fro the noble conqueroure Kynge Arthur for to treate with that tyraunt for his lyege peple.'

'Fy on suche treatys,' sayd she. 'He setteth not by the Kynge ne 115 by no man els. But and yf thou have broughte Arthurs wyf, Dame Gwenever, he shalle be gladder than thow haddest gyven to hym half Fraunce. Beware! approche hym not to nygh, for he hath vaynquysshed xv kynges and hath maade hym a cote ful of precious stones enbrowdred with theyre berdes, whiche they sente hym to have his love for savacion of theyr peple at this 120 laste Crystemasse. And yf thow wylt speke with hym [he is] at yonder grete fyre at souper.'

'Wel,' sayd Arthur, 'I wyll accomplysshe my message for al your ferdful wordes.' And wente forth by the creast of that hylle and sawe where he satte atte souper gnawynge on a lymme of a 125 man, bekynge his brode lymmes by the fyre and brecheles—and thre fayr damoysels tornynge thre broches wheron were broched twelve yonge children late borne lyke yonge byrdes.

Whanne Kynge Arthur beheld that pyteous syghte he had grete compassion on them so that his hert bledde for sorowe, and 130 hayled hym sayeng in this wyse: 'He that alle the world weldeth gyve the shorte lyf and shameful dethe; and the devyl have thy soule. Why hast thow murthred these yonge innocent children and murthred this duchesse? Therfore aryse and dresse the, thow gloton, for this day shall thou dye of my hand.' 135

Thenne the gloton anone starte up and tooke a grete clubbe in his hand and smote at the Kynge that his coronal fylle to the erthe. And the Kynge hytte hym ageyn that he carf his bely and cutte of his genytours that his guttes and his entraylles fylle doune to the ground. Thenne the gyaunt threwe awey his clubbe 140 and caught the Kynge in his armes that he crusshyd his rybbes. Thenne the thre maydens knelyd doune and callyd to Cryst for helpe and comforte of Arthur. And thenne Arthur weltred and wrong that he was otherwhyle under and another tyme above. And so weltryng and walowynge they rolled doune the hylle tyl 145 they came to the see marke, and ever as they soo weltred Arthur smote hym with his daggar. And it fortuned they came to the place where as the two knyghtes were and kepte Arthurs hors.

Thenne when they sawe the Kynge fast in the gyaunts armes they came and losed hym. And thenne the Kynge commaunded 150 Syr Kaye to smyte of the gyaunts hede and to sette it upon a truncheon of a spere and bere it to Syre Howel and telle hym that his enemy was slayne. 'And after late this hede be bounden

to a barbycan that alle the peple may see and behold hit. And go
155 ye two up to the montayn and fetche me my sheld, my suerd and
the clubbe of yron. And as for the tresour take ye it for ye shalle
fynde there good oute of nombre. So I have the kertyl and the
clubbe, I desyre no more. This was the fyerst gyaunt that ever I
mette with sauf one in the mount of Arabé whiche I overcame;
160 but this was gretter and fyerser.'

Thenne the knyghtes fette the clubbe and the kyrtyl, and some
of the tresour they took to them self; and retorned ageyne to the
host. And anone this was knowen thurgh alle the countrey
wherfor the peple came and thanked the Kynge.

165 And he sayd ageyne: 'Yeve the thanke to God and departe the
goodes among yow.' And after that Kynge Arthur sayd and
commaunded his cosyn Howel that he shold ordeyne for a
chirche to be bylded on the same hylle in the worship of Saynte
Mychel.

VII. **Blanchardin and Eglantine** (1489)

Blanchardin wins the love of Eglantine

[Blanchardin in quest of ventures comes to a river which is the boundary of a land, the capital of which is Tormaday. The knight of the ferry tells him that the queen, Eglantine, scorns love and has refused the pagan king Alymodes, who in revenge is about to wage war on her. Eglantine herself is on her way home to Tormaday. The knight urges Blanchardin to win Eglantine's love; to do this he should first win a kiss by some stratagem. Blanchardin promises to try.]

BLANCHARDYN bygan to ryde on a good paas desiring with all
his herte to overtake the proude pucell in amours for to fulfylle
his desyre and the promesse that he made to the knyght. So
thought he moche in hym self by what manere he myght execute
5 and brynge at an ende the werke that he hath undertaken, that is
to wyte to kysse the proude mayden in amours. Wherof in this
manere of thoughte was his noble herte all affrayed and replenysshed wyth grete fere lest he shold faylle of his entrepryse,

for wel it was th'advis of Blanchardyn that the thyng ought well to be putte in a proffe syth his promesse was thus made to the 10 knyght. And for this cause entred wythin his thoughte a drede as for to be so hardy that he sholde vaunce hym self for to kysse suche a pryncesse that never he had seen byfore, and wherof th'acquentaunce was so daungerouse. But Love that wyth her dart had made in his herte a grete wounde admonested hym for 15 to procede constantly to his hyghe entrepryse. And after all varyablenes and debates ybrought at an ende wythin the mynde of this newe lover, his resolucion fynall was that he sholde putte peyne for to have a cusse of the proude pucelle in amours al thoughe deth sholde be unto him adjudged onely for this cause. 20 And herupon went Blanchardyn sayenge: 'O veraye God, how well happy shold myn herte be that presently is overmoche pressed bycause of myn enterpryse, yf I myght obteyne that one cussynge. And yf myn infortune or feblenes of corage sholde lette me fro this adventure that so sore I desyre, deth make an ende of me.' 25

Thus, as ye here, the jovencell Blanchardyn went stryvyng in herte for fere that he had lest he myght not brynge his entrepryse at an ende. And rode thus thynkinge a goode while tyl that soone after he herde the bruyt and the voyces of the proude pucelle in amours folke. And in tornynge of a narowe waye, by the 30 knowlege that the Knyght of the Fery had yeven to hym of her araye, knewe that it was she that he went sekynge and thought it was tyme to endevoyre hym self. He gaf the spore to the hors and forced hym as moche as he coude for to overtake the fayre pucelle, soo that by his dylygence taken wyth an ardaunt desyre 35 fonde hym self nyghe her and of her maystres wythin a short space of tyme. Blanchardyn seeyng the oure and the poynt that he sholde furnysshe hys enterpryse that ful sore he desyred to fynysshe smote hys courser wyth the spore for to kysse her as he furth by her went. Wherof happed by the bruyt that his hors 40 made that she loked bakward for to se what he was that so hastely rode after her. And so well it fortuned Blanchardyn that bothe theyre mouthes recountred and kyst eche other fast.

Yf Blanchardyn was right glad of this adventure it is not to be axed. And of that other party the proude mayden in amours 45

coude not kepe her behavoure in this byhalve for the grete dys-
pleasyre that she toke therfore. But Blanchardyn wyth a glad
chere waloped his courser as bruyauntly as he coude thurghe the
thykkest of all the folke, lepyng alwaye here and there as hors
50 and man had flowen in th'ayer.[1] And dyde so moche in a short
while that he had passed ladyes and damoselles, knyghtes and
squyers and all the grete companye of this proude pucelle in
amours, gyvyng a gracyouse and honourable salutacion to them
all where he went forth by. It is not to be axed yf he was well
55 loked upon of all them of the rowte, and in especiall of the ladyes
and gentyl women that all in one sayde he was a knyght right
goode and fayre and that it semed wel by countenance to be a
man comen of hyghe extraction, merveyllyng hem self what he
myght be and fro whens he came there thus alone wythout eny
60 companye.

Whan Blanchardyn sawe that he had brought at an ende his
enterpryse and that he had passed alle the rowtes and compaynes
of the proude pucelle in amours, he was ryght glad of this fayre
adventure. Soo toke his waye as right as he coude as was tolde
65 hym by the knyght and rode toward Tourmaday. A lytyl shal
here ceasse oure matere to speke of hym unto tyme and oure shal
be for to retourne to the same, and shal shewe the sorowes and
the complayntes of the proude pucelle in amours and the manyere
that she kept after the kysse that Blanchardyn toke of her.

70 Incontynente that she felte her self to be thus sodaynly kyst of a
man, straunger out of her knowlege, she fell doune from here
amblere as a woman from her self and in a swone. And whan she
myght speke, [said] unto her maystres that he that this injurye
had doon to her what so ever he be, yf he may come in her handes
75 or in her power noon shal mowe save hym; but he shal lese his
hed for the same. Of the teerys that from her eyen fyll doune her
gowne that she had on was therof charged as grete shoure of
rayne had come doune from the hevens. Thenne her maystres,
that sage and dyscrete was, conforted her blamyng gretly the
80 grete sorowe that she made for a cusse. But the proude pucelle in
amours kept so hard that same kisse in her corage, whiche she

[1] fowgthen in the thayer

reputed for an injurye doon to her, that fayre speche nor non excusacion that her goode ma[y]stres coude make nor shewe to her for to pease her of her anger myght not in nothynge conforte her; but semed that she sholde slee her self to be more hastely 85 venged.

Her maystres saide unto her: 'Alas, my goode damoyselle, I have right grete merveylle how a prynces of so grete renomme as ye be of may make so grete a sorowe of a thynge of nought. Yf a gentyl man hath kyst you, take we hit for a folye or dis- 90 honoure whiche is not so? Noon but I have seen it and make no doubte that evere hit sholde be discovered nor knowen by me. Soo pray I you that ye wyl cesse your grete sorowe.'

Thenne ansuered the pucell to her maystres: 'How may ye requyre me to leve myn anger, but that I sholde complayne me? 95 No lenger may suffre me God to lyve in suche a sorowe, yf that shame done to me be not right sone avenged. Now knowe I not yf he be a gentyl man or not. Alas, that my knyghtes knowe not and my folke that marchen byfore me this adventure; soone ynoughe they wolde avenge me. Certaynly I shal doo folow hym. 100 And byleve for certayn that his laste daye is comen and shal deye.'

'O madame,' said the maystresse unto the yonge damysell, 'ye shal do more wyseli. For yf thys thynge shuld come oute and be knowen, your sorow ought to double sore therfor. Yf men sayden that of everi man ye had taken a kysse, yet ought ye to maynten 105 and holde th'apposite, saynge strongly ayenst hit. And ye wyll scandalyze and uttre your mysfal that is now happed to you of one man. Lepe upon your palfraye—your folke ben ferre afore you—and put out of your ymaginacyon suche casuall fryvolles and that overmoche do greve your self; for it is for your best and 110 worship grete, yf ye wol understande hit well.'

After many shewynges[1] that the olde damoyselle had don unto her lady, the proude pucelle in amours, wyth what peyne and grief that it was, atte th'ynstance and requeste of her sayde maystresse she mounted anon upon her whyte palfray amblyng; 115 and sayde she sholde fynde at Tourmaday hym that had doon her this vyolence and that by the morowe next she sholde make

[1] shewyngcs

him to be hanged. Sore troubled of wyttis and gretly vexed wythin her mynde, as ye here, rode forthe the gentel pucelle 120 after her folke towardes her cyte of Tourmaday. . . .

[At Tormaday Blanchardin lodges with the Provost, who has two beautiful daughters. Immediately after Eglantine's return the city is besieged by Alymodes, a rejected suitor. The Provost provides Blanchardin with horse and armour; and Blanchardin agrees to wear a black sleeve of one of the Provost's daughters in his helmet.]

After that the Provoste and Blanchardyn were armed of all peces and set upon the myghty coursers, the shelde at the necke, theire helmes bokled and eythre of them the spere in the hande, toke leve of hem that were there and departed out of the place. 125 And cam to the towne gate where they fonde thre thousaund men al redy for to yssue out, the whiche by the motion and warnyng of the Provoste had appareylled them self for to kepe hym felawship and folowe hym. When the Provoste was come to the yate hit was soone open thurghe whiche they alle yssued 130 out in goode and fayre ordynaunce. Blanchardin, whiche was sore desyryng for to prove hym self and shewe his strengthe and vertue to have bruyt and comendacion and that he myght be knowen, dyde putte hym self in the forefront havyng a ryght bygge spere in his hande. They bygan alle to vaunce and marche 135 forth out of the barres of the towne and syth all at ones gaaf a grete crye, wherof theire enmyes that all redy awayted there for them were alle affrayed. They byganne thenne to renne one upon other by so grete strengthe that for the noyse and sowne that the erthe gaffe bycause of the horses that ranne harde upon, it semed 140 to them of wythin and wythout that the foure elementes had fought theire togydre. The duste rose up fro the grounde that derked the lyght of the sonne wyth the shot that drawe was of bothe sides one parte ayenst that other.

Blanchardyn, that in the forefronte was, the first man of all 145 had his spere in the rest and ranne upon Corbadas that nevewe was to Kynge Alymodes, and so grete a stroke and so hevy he gaffe hym that the sperehed appiered at the backe thurgh the body of the sayd Corbadas, and in pulling ageyn his spere he overthrew him doune sterke ded to the erthe. And syth anone he

rought another of Kynge Alymodes knyghtes in suche a wyse 150
that he made his spere to entre his body thurghe lunge and lyvre
and so kyld hym. And so moche he made atte the first emprayynte
that ar evere his swerde was broken he threwe doune ded syx of
his enemyes from their sadelles, the whiche emonge the horses
fete fynisshed myserably theyre dayes. And syn aftre he lyghtly 155
dyde sette hande on the swerde of the whiche he smote here and
there wyth bothe his handes by suche a strengthe that him that he
rought wyth full stroke was all tobrused and cloven in two peces.
He detrenched and kutte bothe horses and knyghtes, he clove
and rent helmes and sheldes, and brake the grete routes and made 160
his enemyes to sprede abrode. Moche better he semed to be a
man of the fayré than a creature of the worlde. All fled byfore
hym and made hym waye to passe. There was noo man how
hardy that he was that durste mete hym so sore fered and doubted
hym his enmyes. Wythin a lytyl whyle he made so moche of 165
proesse that his enemyes were therof ryght sore abasshed and
that his swerde was well beknowen emonge hem—ryght grete
and horryble was the battaylle—and so moche that they of
Tourmaday and his enemyes merveylled gretly of the grete
strengthe and hyghe proes that they sawe in Blanchardyn, the 170
whiche his enmyes fledde as the larke doth the sperhauke.

The howlyng and the noyse bygan to ryse up a hyghe and so
moche that the fayre proude mayden in amours, that lened atte
a wyndowe seeyng the grete proesses and merveyllouse faytes of
armes that by Blanchardin were there made, asked of her maystres 175
that was nyghe her yf she knowe not the knyght that had his hors
coverid with whit rayment; and syth she also perceyved the
black sleve that upon his helmet was sette fast. Her maystres
thenne wyst not what to thynke nor also what he myght be, but
well ynough sayde that he was the most valyaunt and that dyde 180
best that day of al bothe partyes. And she sayde: 'A madame,
loke, nowe ye may see that they all fle awaye byfore hym and ye
may well perceyve that no man dare abyde hym. Moche grete
desyre I have to wyte and knowe what he may be.'

Even atte this oure that the proude mayden in amours and her 185
maystres were in suche talkyng came unto them a squyer that

cryed on hyghe and sayde: 'O my right redoubted lady, yonder wythout may you chuse and see the floure of knyghthode, the subduer and sleer of your enemyes, not yet satysfyed nor fylled
190 of the deth of many of hem but styl destroyeth them. He heweth and felleth doune right al byfore hym. His armes were not longe syth all clere and whyt, but now they be dyed in red wyth the blode of your enemyes that he hath slayne and brought to deth. Madame, knowe for a trouthe that it is the fayre knyght whiche
195 is lodged at the Provostis house.'

When the proude lady in amours understode the squyer speke thus, the bloode ranne up at her face and wexed red as a rose. Well perceyved hit her sayde maystres and that the love of hym smote her, but no semblaunt she made therof to her. Right gladde
200 and joyeful was the pucelle whan she knewe that it was Blanchardyn and bygan to thynke in her self that he was wel worthy to be beloved. Thenne she sayde to her maystres: 'Certes that knyght that I see yonder dooth merveylles of armes. I see the Provost that of nyghe foloweth him; it is to be thought that he shal wyl give
205 him one of his doughters in mariage with a grete parte of his grete havoyre. But on my fayth it were dommage, for he is a man of noble corage and right valyaunt and nought it is to be doubted but that he is come of som noble hous.'

The maystres, that right sage was, dyd perceyve incontynent
210 by her wordes that her indygnacion and evyll wylle that she byfore that had conceyved ayenst Blanchardyn was moderat in her herte, and wyst not what she therof shold thynke but that love had overcome her evyll erroure; wherof she shold have ben right glad. And lyke as her thought was to be, so it was in
215 dede happed. Among other comynyng and devyses that she myght more playnly knowe how it was therof right subtyly bygan to saye thus to the proude pucelle in amours. 'Madame, as for this I knowe and can perceyve youre pryde shal be cause, but yf ye take hede, of the totall distruction of your royalme.
220 Concedere you not that ye be occasion and the cause movyng of th'assemble of the ostis that are for your towne and of the shedyng of bloode that procedeth therof? Yf ye[1] wolde wedde

[1] yf

the Kynge Alymodes all your lande shal be in surete, quyete and peas.' Than the proude mayden in amours after this exhortyng herde of her maystres sayde that she sholde noo more speke 225 therof unto her and that never the dayes of her lyff she sholde wedde paynem nor noo man infydele.

And for this cause cessed a while their talkyng and loked bothe toward the felde where they saw the knyg[h]tes ful sore fyghtyng of bothe partyes. But Blanchardyn hath the praysyng over hem 230 alle, for ther was no man of nother syde that of prowes and worthynes coude go beyonde hym. Wherof Kynge Alymodes knyghtes had grete envye over hym and grete cure and laboure toke upon them for to slee hym. But non of them how hardy that he was durste not proche nor nyghe hym, for as many as he 235 myght reche unto he feld hem doune or slew hem and wounded them grevosly. The proude pucelle in amours folke bare them self right wel that day. This bataylle lasted tyl the nyght came. Wherfore Kynge Alymodes, seeyng that he myght not by noo manere putte nor close them fro the cyte bycause of the wyse wyt 240 and worthynes of the goode knyght Blanchardyn that conduyted them, made to sowne and call the retreyte or wythdrawe his men to his losse and grete confusion, and wythdrewe hym self into his tente right wrothe and sorowfull for the losse of dyvers his knyghtes—and all thurgh the vertue and strengthe of one knyght 245 onely.

Blanchardyn and the Provost wyth theire folke wyth grete glorye and tryumphe entred ayen into the cyte and brought wyth them many a riche prysonner. And to the Provostis house toke Blanchardyn his waye, wherunto he was conveyed of the 250 most parte of the noble men makyng to hym the gretest honoure that men can or may doo to a knyght, as to hym that best had doon that day. And to saye the trouthe many of the gretest of hem had ben slayn or taken yf by the vertue and strengthe of Blanchardyn they had not be socoured and holpen that day. 255 Some he helped ayen upon theire horses whan they were feld doune, some he rescued from the hande of theire enmyes that had hem as prysoners. So bare him self that wyth grete tryumphe and grete glorye he retourned fro the bataylle wyth them unto the

260 sayde Provostes place to the grete benyvolence and gladnesse of the peple of the cyte, and there alyghted from his hors and the Provost wyth hym whos two doughters that were right fayre and praty came there ayenst them. For bothe of hem loved sore Blanchardyn and right enamored they were over hym. There 265 abode xx knyghtes at souper wyth Blanchardyn for to chere and feste hym and to be acoynted of hym. Harpe, lute, sawtrye and dyverse other instruments of melodyouse musyke were sent for, for to rejoysshe the noble felawship that was full fayre. For there were comen diverse ladyes, many a gentyl woman, maydens and 270 noble bourgeyses at the requeste and prayers of the Provoste and of his two doughters that were right besy for to chere and serve Blanchardyn wyth all dyligence.

Atte the same owre that this joye and feste was in makyng in the Provostis house, the proude pucelle in amours was in her 275 castel lenyng upon one of her chambre wyndowes that had syght wythin the towne and herde the noyse and the feste that was adoyng in the Provostis house for love of Blanchardyn and for to doo hym worshipe and honoure, wherof she was advertysed alredy. And how be it that as ye have herde anone she had gyven 280 her self in hir herte to the sayd Blanchardyn, alle wayes at the same owre was taken the fynall and faste conclusion and altogydre was of her determyned to make of Blanchardyn her lover and her specyall, that a lytyl before that for one kysse onely was so ferre from her gode grace and in daunger of his lyf yf[1] the God-285 desse of Love that is so myghty of her grace had not purveyed better for hym. At the begynnyng of this new alyaunce, Amoures or Love served her wyth a messe sharp and sowre ynoughe tyl her tast, that is to wyte of a lovely care that is as moche worthe as a suspecyouse jalousye of the doughters of the Provoste and her 290 specyall, Blanchardyn. But she thought in her self that she sholde purvey therto of a remedye mete and goode to the cause, whiche thynge she dyde as ye shal here herafter. Love, that departeth wyth her goodes where as it semeth her best employed, forgate not her newe servaunt but atte her first comyng made her to be 295 vysited and wayted upon by a servant of hers, named Care, that

[1] of

well sore movyd and troubled her spyrites. And she that was not lernyd to receyve suche geestes, sore harde was his queyntaunce to her. And yet wythin a whyle after Love smote her ayen wyth a darte to the quycke tyll the herte of her, so that the fayer pucell wyst not her behavyng nor how to mayntene her self and also 300 had no power to drynke nor ete nor coude not slepe ne take no maner of reste, but held her hert so esprised and so overpressid wyth love that she had to Blanchardyn that she myght noo lenger hyde her falle. Thenne cam to her maystres and said to her in thys maner: 'Alas, who shall mowe recover helth to this pacient 305 sore syke that suffreth wyth goode wyll of herte both grete thurste, honger and shaketh for colde caused thrughe a hete intollerabyll?'

The maystres perceyved anoone by her wordes and maner that she had ben in the chapiter of the God of Love and by his grace 310 men shuld have gode accompte of the pryde that overlonge a tyme had ruled her dismesurable herte. She thought that she had ben taken wyth Kyng Alymodes love and syth said unto her: 'Madame, ye oughte to yelde grete graces and thankes to the myghty God of Love, seyng the unknoulege that ye have had 315 alwayes here byfore of his vertues, that hath dayned to vysite you and to altre and change your corage. I byleve now that for cause of thys soudayn mutacion ye be seke and sore passioned of one accident that nameth hym self the sore of love.'

'Alas,' said the pucell, 'the sore of love is ryght anguyssous and 320 hevy for to bere, as me semeth.'

'Madame,' sayd her maystres, 'men must suffre for better to have. This evyll shalle be cause of your perfeccion, and knouleche that love is that thynge that moost embellisheth and decoreth the nobyl corages. And I can not thynke that ever man and woman 325 havyng bruyt or name of some goode vertues passyng other have come nor raughte therunto wythoute that they were or had ben in the service of Love.'

The proude mayden in amours herkened hir maystres. But the fevere that Love had tak[e]n her for to plucke oute the roote of 330 pryde from her herte lettid here sore, and atte the ende of a whyle biganne to saye: 'Alas, Amours, I have longe defendyd my sylf ayenst the harde assautes and impetuous excitacions that often tymes thy messangers made unto me. Now have I nother power 335 nor wyl to defende me eny more; unto the I yelde me.'

VIII. **Paris and Vienne** (1485)

How the suit of the Duke of Burgundy's son was thwarted

[Vienne, the daughter of the Dauphin, falls in love with Paris, the son of one of her father's nobles, and promises that she will marry no one but him. Her father, however, wants her to marry someone of higher rank and arranges a match with the Duke of Burgundy's son. Vienne, considering herself betrothed to Paris, refuses him and is imprisoned by her father.]

WHAN the sone of the Duc of Bourgoyne had abyden longe tyme in hys contree, on a day he had grete thought of Vyenne and that was for the grete beaute of hyr; and it dysplesed hym moche that at hys beyng there he had not seen hyr. And so con- 5 cluded to goo and see hyr. And it was not longe after that he cam to the Dolphyn and the Doulphyn receyved hym moche gladly and with grete honour. Thenne prayed he the Dolphyn that it myght plese hym to shewe to hym Vyenne also seke as she was, for in the world was nothyng that he soo moche desyred to see 10 as hyr. And the Doulphyn seyng the wylle and desyre of hym wold noo lenger hyde hys courage, but sayd to hym: 'My fayr sone, by the fayth that I owe to God I have had grete desyre that thys maryage shold be made. But my doughter for thys present tyme wyl take noo husbond ne be maryed. Wherfore I have grete 15 desplaysyr. And that for the love of you and to th'ende that ye knowe that it holdeth not on me, I swere to you that sythe ye departed fro thys toun I have doon hyr to be kepte in a pryson derke and obscure, and hath eten nothyng but brede and water onely, and have sworn that she shal not goo oute of pryson tyl 20 she shal consente to have you in maryage. And thus I praye you that ye take noo desplaysyr yf at thys tyme ye see hyr not, for ye may not faylle to have grete maryage in caas that this faylle you.'

And thenne he ansuerd: 'Honourable syr, I praye you moche hertely syth that it is so that er I retorne I may speke to hyr. And I shal praye hyr as moche as I shal mowe and shal see yf by ony 25 manere I may converte hyr fro hyr wylle.'

Thenne sayd the Doulphyn he was contente. Thenne he sente to his doughter clothyng and vestymentes for to clothe hyr and also mete for to ete, for in two monethes she had eten but brede and water, wherof she was moche feble; and that shewed wel in 30 her vysage. And thus he dyd bycause she shold consente to the maryage. And thenne it was concluded that the sone of the Duc of Bourgoyn shold come see hyr and speke with hyr.

And thenne whan Vyenne sawe thys and had receyved all and knewe that the sone of the Duc of Bourgoyn shuld come and 35 speke wyth hyr, she said to Ysabeau, hir damoysel: 'Fayr suster, beholde how my fader and moder wene by these vestymentes and thys henne that I shold ete to deceyve me and put me fro my purpoos. But God forbede that I shold do so.' And thenne she took the henne and sayd to hyr that brought it: 'Syth it 40 playseth to the sone of the Duke to come and speke to me, say ye to hym that he may not come these iij dayes, and whan he cometh that he brynge with hym the Bysshop of Saynt Laurens.'

She that had brought to hyr the henne sayd alle thys unto the Doulphyn and to Dame Dyane, hir moder. 45

Thenne Vyenne took the two quarters of the henne and put them under hyr armehooles and helde them there so longe that they stonken moche strongely. And whan it came to the thyrd day, the Bysshop of Saynt Laurence and the sone of the Duke of Bourgoyne camen for to see Vyenne. And or they entred they 50 opened a treylle whyche gaf lyght into the pryson.

Thenne whan the sone of the Duc sawe Vyenne in the pryson, he sayd to hir by grete pyte that he had: 'Noble Vyenne, how wyl ye deye thus for hungre soo folyly by your owne defaulte? And knowe ye not wel that your fader hath gyven you to me to 55 have to my wyf? Wherfore I lyve in grete payne and in moche grete sorowe for the duresse of your courage; wherof ye doo ryght grete synne. And doubte ye not that God punyssheth you for th'ynobedyence that ye doo to your fader and to your moder?

60 Wherfore I praye you, fayre Vyenne, to telle to me for what cause ye wyl not have me in maryage to your husbond. Doubte ye that whan ye shall be wyth me that ye may not serve God as wel as ye now do that suffre thys payne? I promyse you by my fayth that ye shal have playsaunces and lybertees in al the maners
65 that ye shal conne demaunde. Thenne I praye you that ye wyl not here deye so dolorously. And yf ye wyl not doo it for the love of me, yet at the leste do it for the love of your fader and of your moder whyche lyve for you in grete sorowe and in grete hevynesse; wherfore ye ought to have pyte on them.'

70 Whan Vyenne had herde these wordes she was quasi abasshed and sayd: 'Syr, savyng your honour I am maryed, how be it ye knowe hym not whome I have in myn hert. And also I knowe and graunte ryght wel that ye be worthy to have one moche gretter and more hye a lady than I am. And I late you wete that
75 for hym that I desyre I shold suffre more payne than I fele. And therfore I praye you that fro hensforth ye speke to me no more of thys mater. And also I am so evyl dysposed in my persone that yf it endure in me my lyf shal not be longe; and yf it were honeste I shold shewe it you and than shold ye see how it stondeth
80 wyth me. Nevertheles approche ye ner to me and ye shall the better byleve me.' And the sone of the Duke of Bourgoyne and the Bysshop of Saynt Laurence approuched unto Vyenne, fro whom yssued soo grete a stenche that unnethe they myght suffre and endure it; whiche savour came fro under hyr armeholes of
85 the two quarters of the henne, whiche were roten. And whan Vyenne sawe that they had felte ynough of the stenche, she sayd to them: 'Lordes, ye may now knowe ynough in what adventure I am dysposed.'

Thenne they took leve havyng grete compassyon on hyr. And
90 they sayd to the Dolphyn that Vyenne was thenne half roten and that she stanke and demed in them self that she myght not lyve longe and that it shold be grete damage of hyr deth for the soverayn beaute that was in hyr. And incontynent the sone of the Duc of Bourgoyn took hys leve of the Doulphyn and retorned
95 into hys contrey, and recounted to hys fader the lyf of Vyenne, wherof alle they that herde hym had grete pyte in theyr herte.

IX. The Metamorphoses of Ovid (1480)

The transformation of Philomela

[When the barbarians attacked Athens, Tereus, King of Thrace, came to help Pandion, King of Athens, and was instrumental in their defeat.]

WHAN the warre was fynysshed Pandeon gaf to Thereus one of hys two doughters whyche were named Phylomena and Prone. But the Kynge of Trace requyred Prone in mariage; and Pandeon gaf her to hym gladly. But for this maryage sourded after grete inconveniencis, grete tribulacions, and deth of men. 5
This weddyng were evyl: Hymeneus, God of Weddynge, was not there, ne there was no joye. But al nyght were on the chambre Ledus the owle, the cuckowe, the raven, and the crowe, whyche was sygnefyance of sorowe and hevynes. Atrops and Thezyphone and alle evylle destynees flewe al nyghte by the 10
chambres and the halles of the palays. Whan the weddyng was fynysshed and that the kynges, prynces, and barons, ladyes, and damoyselles were departed fro the cite of Athenes, Thereus lade hys wyf into hys royame of Trace.

They hade in an yll tyme bytwene them bothe a sone, which 15
hade to name Ytys; whyche lyved not longe tyme as shal be sayde after what befyl of hym. The daye of his burthe was halowed by the comandement of Thereus thrughout al the royame, a grete feste made, and every yere made as apperteyned to a kynges sone. 20

Prone had ben wyth her husbonde v yere and moo, whan on a daye after certayn wordes she prayde hym that she myghte goo and see her suster Phylomena, yf hyt plesed hym; and yf hit plesed hym not, that he wold goo hym self and fecch her. He answerd that he wolde goo and fecche her into Trace, hys royame. 25
Thereus garnysshyd his shyppes and entred into them with grete companye, and saylled toward Athenes. The see was peasyble, wherof was grete pyte and domage that he was not drowned, for grete scathes and domages hade thenne not be don. He arryved atte porte of Athenes. 30

Pandeon, that herde of thise tydyngis, wente ayenst hym and fested gretly hys gendre Thereus and hys peple, and lade hym into his cite. And after demanded tydyngis of his doughter Prone and of her sone. Thereus[1] answerde that they were hole and in
35 good poynt and moch humbly comanded them to hym. And after tolde hym th'occasyon of his comyng: how Prone had grete desyre to see and speke with her suster Phylomena. And prayde hym that he wolde sende her thyder, promettynge that after she hade ben there a daye or two, and hade good wynde and propyce,
40 he sholde brynge her agayn. 'And I complayne me also that I have not seen her.'

Out of a chambre yssued thenne Phylomena alle bare-heeded. The tongue of Plato ne the wysedom of Salamon myght not suffyse ne wryte ne saye her ryght grete beaute. Nature had en-
45 forced to gyve and make her fayre of many a grace and to gyve her more beawte than to ony other. And she was no lasse wyse than fayre. She cowde al maner dysportes: playe atte chesse and tables, hunte with houndes, and knewe the crafte of hawkyng with sperhawkes, fawcons gentyl, lanyers and other, and cowde
50 late them flee at the ryver. And she cowde passynge wel werke purple bawdkyns and pourtraye in cloth[2] what that ever she wolde. And she was wel lettred and of al maner instrumentis she cowde entremete. And she coude so wysly speke that she coude holde a scole.

55 The mayde cam to her fader. And Thereus embraced and kyssed her whyche anon was esprysed with her love for her beaute and her fayr contenance as soone as he sawe her. Love made hym to dote whan that he sette hys herte on the suster of his wyf to love her. Nevertheles, after the lawe that tho was holde,
60 it was no vylonye: and therof myghte Thereus excuse hym, for one of their goddes establisshed and ordeyned that they myghte do their playsyr and wylle on whom it lyked them. Suche lawe helde tho the paynems. But late us leve al this: ther is none that may withsto[n]de love. In an evyl tyme yssued Thereus out of
65 Trace for to fecche Phylomena, for love surprysed hym for her in suche wyse that it myght be no more.

[1] Theseus [2] cloþ

Thereus toke the mayde in his armes and sayde to her thus: 'Phylomena, swete frende, your suster saleweth you and prayeth you that ye wolde come and see her. And I also praye you. Ye had ben longe seen in Trace yf ye myghte have ben there by 70 wysshinge, for Prone maketh prayer ne wysshe ne desyreth nothynge but to have you there. And but yf I hade reteyned her by force, she hade now ben here with yow. And at my departynge she sayde playnly that I sholde never be her lorde ne husbonde yf I broughte not you with me into Trace. And certaynly I hade 75 lever be olde, feble, and hoore than she sholde make me such chere. Wherfore I praye you that ye praye my lord your fader that he suffre you to com with me. I hope it shal not greve hym to late you come and see your suster.'

'Sire,' sayde Phylomena, 'my prayere availleth not so moche as 80 youris; ye sholde praye yf ye wolde obteyne. And yf ye wyl not praye your self, make some other damoyselle to praye for yow.'

'Ye say[1] trouthe,' sayde Thereus, 'but ye oughte to demande me yf I have prayd.'

Phylomena answerde: 'Why? Have ye spoken to hyme of this 85 mater?'

'Ye,' said he, 'but he ansuerde me not.'

'Thenne,' saide she, 'syth that he gaf you none answere, this request pleseth hym not. My suster may longe abyde, for she shal not see me yet.' 90

'Wherby knowe ye?' sayde Thereus.[2] 'He graunteth that answerth not.'

T'his sentence,' sayde the mayde, 'is not verytable, for yet be we in doubte whether he wyl graunte or gaynsaye it.'

Thenne saide Thereus to Pandeon: 'Sire Kyng, ye have wel 95 herd my message fro youre doughter by me and for her ye sholde doo more than for alle the men of the worlde, for to praye yow for this requeste I travaylle at her commandement.'

Pandeon, to whom this mater noyed[3] and grevyd, answerde: 'Frende, I have nothinge in this worlde but ye maye have it, yf 100 ye have nede or to doo withall. But I trowe yf ye knewe the goodes that Phylomena my doughter doth to me, as long as I

[1] sayde [2] Thezeus noyer

sholde lyve ye wolde not requyre me of that ye desyre. I shal not thenne lyve longe. I am olde and feble and have nothyng in this
105 worlde that pleseth me sauf onely my doughter, for by her I lyve. I have none other sustenance. She kepeth and serveth me nyght and daye, and her servyse pleseth me so moche that yf she ne were I hade longe syn bee deede. Ye shal abrigge my lyf yf ye take her fro me away. And therfore I praye yow, of this requeste
110 late me be quyte.'

For this ansuere Thereus was so sorowfull that a grete while he coude not speke a worde, and began to syghe and to complayne. Folye vaynquysshed his wytte whan he behelde the mayde. Wel wende he that he shold goo oute of his wytte, yf he exployted
115 [not] to come to hys wylle and desyre, for it laye not in his myghte to leve hys corage. Ofte he embraced the mayde and wepte, syghed, and thoughte never to see the daye to have her at his wylle. And thought by hym self alone that by love he myghte not gete her; and for [to] take her by nyght and carye
120 her awaye by force and strengthe he hade not peple ynoughe with hym. He hade doon overmoche folye yf he wold have mevyd and stormed the cyte. For this cause al that he myghte he hydde this mater and dyssymyled. And reson put hym fro this thoughte, and sayde that yet he wolde assaye yf he might vaynquysshe by
125 prayer.

Thenne began agayn Thereus to praye Pandeon and sayde in this maner. 'Sire,' sayde he, 'I see wel and knowe that ye wolde doo lytyll for me whan ye have reffused to me my requeste. I have wel loste my labour in this parte, wherof I come to late to
130 repente. I helde me never for so moch a fool for thynge that I ever dyde. Ye have founde poure occasyon for your doughter that servyth you. Have ye not sergeants and maydens ynoughe for to serve yow? Ye may wel have pacyence for iij or iiij dayes, yf ye wyl, and late her come and disporte her with her suster, whyche
135 hath sente me hether for that same cause and that sayde to me whan I departed that I shold never retourne without I brought her suster Phylomena. For I sholde faylle of her love yf I broughte her not. And therfore I wote never what to saye. For yf I shold be exyled of her love, I sholde have grete sorowe for my sone

and yet more for my wyf; and yf I leve Phylomena here, it shall 140
seme to my wyf that I have doon no devoir. Therfore I wepe and
am mervayllously troubled, whan in so lityl a thynge ye fayle me.
Fayre Sire, delyvere her to me and I swere to you by alle the
sayntes on whom I byleve and sette my fayth in ostage that I shal
brynge and rendre her sauf and hoole within xv dayes.' 145

This fals and desloyal traytre dede so moche by wepinge, by
promysynge, and by sweryinge that he exployted even as he
wolde. For Pandeon[1] supposed that he wepte for grete pyte, of
whyche he cowde not hym self absteyne; but wepte wyth hym
and sayde to hym: 'Frende, thou shalt have my doughter to- 150
morowe by suche covenant and promyse that thou hast fyanced
to me. Kepe her wel and brynge her anone ayen. And knowe
thou veryly that her departyng greveth me sore; and I shal never
have joye at my herte unto the tyme that I shal have her agayn
with me.' 155

Thereus promysed al this covenaunt; and wente forwith to
soper wher as they were ryally servyd. But Thereus hade no joye
in ony servyse that he sawe sauf only on the gente body of the
mayde to behold. He thoughte on non other thyng. After soper
everych wente to bedde. Thereus hade lever to have waked and 160
to have spoken with the fayre Phylomena, where he hade sette
all his herte—how wel that none knewe it. For yf she hade
knowen that he had had suche thought and desire as he hade, she
wold never have goon with hym. Thereus might not slepe this
nyght ne reste for folye that so travayllid hym. 165

Whan Thereus herde the wacch of the day sowne, he was
moche joyous. He aroos lyghtly and awaked his peple. Pandeon
for to kepe hym his promyse delyverd hym his doughter Phylomena, whyche was joyous and glade for she supposed shortly to
see her suster and saufly to retourne. The Kynge Pandeon con- 170
veyed them unto the porte and prayde ofte Thereus that he sholde
brynge agayn his doughter at the terme that he hade promysed
to hym. And also said to hys doughter that she sholde thynke
soone to retorne and that she sholde remembre hym, for withoute her he coude not lyve. More [th]an C tymes he sayde to her 175

[1] Pantheon

thise wordes, embracynge and kyssynge her. And atte departynge comanded them to the goddes. And in lyke wyse dyde the traytre to hym. Anon the shyppe was out of syghte by the good wynde that they hade, and Pandeon[1] wepte for his doughter,
180 whome he never sawe after.

When they were descended on the see, Thereus spacke in trayson now of one thyng, now of another, so longe that whan they cam to land he brought her into a wode unto a poure lytyl hows whyche was ferre fro the toun and out of the waye. And
185 whan they were in the hows, they two allone, and that no man myghte see ne here hem, he requyred of companye with her. She that was abasshed defended her self with wordes and wythsayde hym. But whan he sawe that by prayer he might not have his wylle, he enforced her, defowled and corrupte her—wherof
190 she was as sorowful as she might be. She cessed not to sorowe and wepe. Thereus not content of this that he had don to [her], thenne that Phylomena sholde never shewe this matere to man ne to woman, dyde doo drawe the tongue out of her mouthe and cutt it of.

195 This tyrant exployted evyl in this dede and also on that other. And after this he lefte her closed and shette in that lytyll hows wepynge and toterynge her fayre heere. Of this deceyt Thereus dyde grete folye. And for to kepe her he sette an olde woman, a vylayne, whyche lyved by her labour. She coud spynne and weve;
200 and had a doughter with her whyche lerned her crafte. Thereus commanded her that in no wyse the damoyselle sholde goo out of the hows, and that she doo to her al that apperteyneth. She promysed and sware to hym that she sholde so doo. And he trusted her and departed and cam to hys peple, whyche knewe
205 wel of this fayte, but they doubted hyme so moche that they durst not saye one worde. And thus they hydde this dede more for dredde than for love.

T[h]ereus and hys folke cam into Trace. Prone, that supposed tha[t] Phylomena hade come, gladly and joyously went for to
210 mette with hem. But whan she sawe her not, hit plesed her nothyng to heere ne welcome theym, but as abasshyd and affrayed

[1] Pantheon

demanded wher her suster was, and what she made, and who withhelde her that she cam not for to see her. The traytre made semblant of sorowe and dangerous for to answere. And said to her aftirwarde that she hade not to doo for to knowe. And she 215 thenne the more prayd hym for to telle her, or ellis she wolde passe over the see for to goo and see her. Thenne Thereus, makynge sygne of sorowe and hevynes, sayde that she was deede. Whan Prone herde thise tydyngis she was discomforted so grevously that it is mervaylle to reherce. She cursyd the goddes 220 and the deth; and sithe prayde hem that they wolde take her also, and she wold pardone them. And after sayde that ever after in remembrance of this sorowe she wold were clothes of blacke colour; and so she dyde. And she comanded to brynge to her two bulles for to sacrefyse unto the goddes. She made sacrefyse unto 225 Pluto, God of Helle, requyrynge hym to kepe the sowle of her sustir in worshyp. And whan she hade made her sacrefyce, she comanded to make a fyre in the temple. Suche custome the kynges maynteyned in that tyme and dyde such folyes for theyre parents and their frendes. 230

Thus prayde Prone for the sowle of Phylomena her suster, whyche was not deede but lyved, and every daye renewed her sorowe for the traytre that had don by force alle hys wylle of her. Phylomena desyred sore that her suster shold knowe of her estate. But she wyste not by what engyne she myghte late her have 235 knowleche of it, for messager hade she none that myght goo. And also she hade no tongue for to saye ne speke a word for to descovere and to telle her corage and message, yf she one hade had. And on that other syde, she hadde no leyser ne leve for to yssue out of the hows, for the olde vylayne alway was by her. 240 She thought for to werke in a curtyne in whyche she sholde manyfeste and shewe to Prone her suster al her evyll aventure. She made swyftly her werke. She wente to a coffre where the olde vylayne hade put her threde, blewe, yelowe, grene, and of al colours. But she knewe not what werke she made and wrought,[1] 245 wherfor she lete her werke and gaf to her colours suche as she desyred and were behoveful for suche a werke. Whyche werk

[1] worought

was fayr and plesed her wel, how be it it was grevous to make. Atte one of the endes she hade tyssued howe Phylomena hade
250 made it. After this was pourtrayed the shypp wherin Thereus passed the see whan he wente to fecche her in Athenes, and how [he] behaved hym whan he was come, and how he brought her and enforced her, and how he had lefte her in the hous in the woode where she was emprysoned. After this how he hade cutte of her
255 tongue.

Whan Phylomena hadde achyeved this werk she was moche reconforted of her annoye and gryef. She thought who myghte bere it to her suster, her hostesse or her doughter; there were no moo but they thre in the hows. Phylomena hade ben there vij
260 monethis that never mevyd oute of the hows, in whych tyme her hostesse knew and understoode her by sygnes. And she never gaynsayde thynge to her sauf only th'yssue and goynge out of the hous, for Thereus hade that deffended. Hyt happed on a day that Phylomena with her maistresse loked out of the wyndowe and
265 never tofore she came to dore ne wyndowe sith Thereus hade defended it. And there as she laye in the wyndowe she sawe throughe the woode and the ryver the cyte wher her suster dwelled. Thenne she began strongly to wepe, as she that coude not be comforted of her sorowe. Her ma[i]stresse hade grete
270 pytie and gladly wolde have recomforted her yf she hade myghte and graunted to her[1] alle thynges reservyd the yssue of the hows.

Whan Phylomena had apperceyvyd that was don to her al her playsyr, whan she sawe her tyme, she wente and fette the curtyne that she hade tyssued and wrought, and sythe cam to her mais-
275 tresse that knew al her sygnes as wel as she hade spoken with her mouth and made sygne to her that she shold sende this courtyne by her doughter and present it[2] to the Quene of the cyte. She understode it anone and thought that she sholde have therby som rewarde or gwerdon, and doubted nothynge. But charged her
280 doughter therwith and sayde: 'Doughter, bere this unto the Quene and presente it to her, and that don retorne anon agayn.'

Phylomena was tho moch recomforted whan she sawe the courtyne borne forth and hoped therby to have socoure. The

[1] hȳ [2] presentid

mayde taryed not tyl she cam to the Quene and presente to her the courtyne. The Quene behelde it ententyvely and knew wel 285 the werke, but she dyscovered not her thought ne wold not crye ne make noyse. She comanded her that brought it that she goo home agayn; and so she dyde. The Quen folowed her aferre withoute losynge the syghte of her, in such wyse as the mayde apperceyved it not, unto the tyme that she was entred into the 290 lytyl hows. Thenne the Quene, as mad or out of her wytte, cam to the hows whyche was fast shette and smote the dore with her foot withoute spekyng of ony worde. And the olde woman helde her stelle and spake not. And Phylomena ran for to have opend the dore, but the vylayn that trembled for dredd reteyned her. 295 And Prone smote and knocked so hard that at laste she bracke the dore open. And the olde woman that durst not abyde fledde and hydde her in a chambre.

Thenne came Prone in al araged cryenge 'Phylomena, wher art thou? Be not aferde, I am thy suster Prone.' Thenne came 300 Phylomena unto her withoute taryenge. And Prone toke her in her armes and kyssed her, whyche almost for sorow wente out of her wytte.[1] 'Suster,' sayde she, 'come with me, ye have ben over-longe here. In an unhappy day was it whan the fel traytre wedded me, whyche also hath you enforced, defloured and in suche wyse 305 defowled that to me ye may not speke.' Thenne departed the dam-oyselles toward the cyte without holdynge waye or path tyl Prone brought her suster into a chambre under erthe for more secretly to make theyre sorowe. Ther sayde Prone wepyng to her suster: 'Phylomena, I am hevy and sorowful that I may not avenge yow 310 of the felon traytre that so hath trespaced to yow. The goddes gyve hym hys deserte.'

With this wordes came Ytis her sone to her in an evyl ad-venture, as it happed to hym. Whan the moder sawe her sone, she sayde softly as the devyl counceylled her: 'Ha, a,' sayd she, 315 'thyng lyke unto the felon traytre. For the felonye and forfayt of thy fader thou muste dye withoute cause, for as moch only as I sawe never thyng resemble more to other than thou dost to thy fader.' The chylde that herde nothynge herof ran to her and

[1] wycte

320 kyssyd her. Wel ought Prone to absteyne and put fro her this derke and mortal thought by very ryghte and moderly pyte and love, and that she sholde not slee her sone. But whan she remembred the traytre she sayde that whatsoever happed she wold cut of hys heed and gyve it to hys fader for to ete, and that so she
325 wolde avenge her sorow and her susters whom the felon traytre hade so defowled and deshonoured.

Thenne as the chylde halsed hys moder in chierte, she cutte of hys heed as the devyl counceylled her. And bytwene hem bothe they appoynted and dyghted the flesshe of the chylde, one parte
330 boyled in the pote, and another parte was rosted. And whan it was tyme and oure of dyner, and that the flesshe was soden and rosted, Prone for to fulfylle her wyll came to the Kynge and prayde hym for the love of the thynge that he most loved in the worlde that he wold come and dyne with her allone without ony
335 companye savynge they two; and she wolde serve hym of al thynge.

The Kynge graunte her with a good wylle so that hys sone Ytis sholde be also there. 'Veryly,' sayde Prone, 'he shal be there; and so we thre shal be there togydre—and by my wylle ther shal
340 be no moo. Com whan it pleseth yow, for al thyng is now redy, and we shal make good chiere.'

Thereus knewe not of what mete he shold ete. She broughte hym forth and sette hyme moche playsantly to th'ende that the dyner sholde better plese hym. The place was notably arayed
345 wher the Kyng satte. She broughte hym an haunche of hys sone Ytys, and he began wel to ete therof. And after demanded where hys son Ytis was, and sayd: 'Dame, ye promysed me that he shold be here with us.'

'Syre,' sayde Prone, 'have ye no doubte, for ye shal be anon
350 fylled of hys syghte. He is not fer hens. He shal be here anon.' Thene she wente and fette another hanche.

And Thereus, what he ete and dyde, sayde agayne to Prone: 'Dame, ye holde me not covenant whan ye brynge not to me Ytys. It overmoche greveth me that he cometh not, and I wote
355 not whome I may sende for hym but yf I goo my self, I pray yow to goo and fecche hym.'

Prone might no lenger abyde ne hyde fro Thereus her lorde of what mete that he ete and wherof she hade servyd hym. But sayde to hym in grete anger: 'False and dysloyal traytre, thou hast of hym that thou demandest for, parte in thy body and parte 360 is withoute.' Wyth this wordes yssued out Philomena of a chambre nygh by where as she hade ben hyde and brought in the heed of the chylde and threwe it in the vysage of Thereus in suche wyse that it bebledde hym.

Thereus sawe thenne that he was betrayed. He was so abasshed 365 a whyle of angwysshe and of shame that he meved not ne spak one worde. Whan he knewe that it was the hede of hys chylde and knewe for trouth that Prone hade gyven hym to hym for to ete and that he sawe Phylomena, he shoof the table from hym and caste al doun and toke a swerde for t'avenge the deth of hys 370 sone, whyche was hangynge on the walle. But the two susters tho durst there no lenger abyde, for he chaced them for to have slayn them. But thenne as it plesed the destynees befyll the grettest mervayll of the worlde or that tofore hade ben herde. For Thereus became a lapwynch whych is a fowl byrde and a vylayn- 375 ous, for the trayson that he hade don to the damoyselle Phylomena. Prone becam a swalowe and Phylomena became a nyghtyngale. Yet her songe cryeth out upon alle untrew lovers and sayth that they shal be destroyed. And for bycause she hateth them, she syngeth the moost swetly that she can, whan the 380 prymtemps is comen in the buscage, 'Occy, occy, occy'.

Sens hystoryal to the fable

For as moche as Phylomena was so longe shytte up in the woode and hydd and for that she was noble, wyse, prudent, and courtoys, and that so wel cowde synge, is fayned that she was torned into a nyghtyngale. And Prone that had[1] cut hys sones 385 heed fledd for fere of her husbonde and kepte her in a stronge tour. And therfore is fayned that she becam a swalowe whych is yet acustomed to make her neste in hye toures or chemynes. And Thereus for the evyl that he dyde in deceyvynge the mayde Phylomena and for that he hade ben a wyse knyght and a valyant 390

[1] hat

and that he hade bore armes in many bataylles as of habergeon, of sheld, of polax, and of healme wheron were plumettis, therfor fayneth the fable that for hys trayson he becam a lapwynch or huppe whych is a fable byrde and a vylayne.

X. History of Troy (1473/4)

The story of Medusa

IN the lande of Esperye passid out of this world a kynge named Porcus, a man of right grete enterpryse, whyche the Esperiens callyd God of the See of Spaygne, auncyently named Esperye as sayd is. This Kynge lefte thre doughtres that had not but oon
5 eye, as the poetes saye, that is to saye that her pryncipall charge was unto the vanytees of the world. And therfore they were callyd Gorgonnes, that is to saye cultyveresses or labourers of the erthe for as moche as they entended unto vyces that behelde erthely thynges. Of thyse doughtres oon was named Meduse,
10 that other Ewryale and the thyrde Scenno. Meduse that was the eldest of that other succeded in th'empyre and in the royame. And the poetes saye that she had hede of a serpent, gyvyng by this to understande that she was souverainly wyse and subtyl. After the deth of Kynge Porcus this Meduse gouverned hyely her
15 royame and held pyrates and men of warre. And in her begynnyng she toke and hauntyd the See of Ewrope in feet, and wyth right grete tryumphe descended on a day at the porte of Att[h]enes and sente unto the Kynge Neptune to requyre him that he wold graunte unto her that she might entre into his cyte
20 for to worshippe in the temple [of] the goddesse Pallas, whiche was newly maad. Neptune dide grete honour unto the messangers of Meduse and accorded unto her that she shold entre into his cite and into the temple, forseen that she shold have none with her save her damoyselles.

25 Whan Meduse herde the answere of Kynge Neptune, she concluded that she wold go into the temple, wherof was a grete renomee, and was acompanyed with many damoiselles so richely

arayed that hit was a tryumphe for to see. She entryd into the temple and into the cyte and ther she torned into stones not only the men that behelde her, but also the women and among all 30 other specially a quene that was named Yde. Bi this hit is to understande that this Meduse was of so[1] excellente beaute and was so passing ryche that all they that behelde her gafe hem self overperfitly to covoyte her beaute and her rychesses. And therfore wryte the poetes that they were torned into stones. For they 35 that dispose them and gyve them to the delices of this world ben lykned and compared unto hard stones wherof may no good come. Thus than Meduse entryng into Athenes convertyd and torned many men into stones in so moche that Neptunus herd these tydynges and desiryng to see this Quene, he wente hym 40 into the temple where she was in contemplacion. And he had not longe beholde her whan he felte hym so covoytous of her and of her love that he said to hym self that she shold be his wif and that she shold never escape hym.

This Meduse was longe space in contemplacion. This duryng 45 Neptune desired her beaulte more and more and his herte juged in hym that he sholde come to his entencion. But anon after that his herte had made this jugement he a lityll debated consideryng the excellence of her. Another jugement traversid and sourded in his entendement that constraynd hym to saye these wordes 50 that folowe. 'Alas, in what matyer, in what sorow and in what right grete and enflamyng payne ben they that ben brennyng in love by longe space of tyme, that I that now begynne fynde me in so many sighes and payne that I wote never how I may in tyme come unto this lady for to requyre her to be my wyf. She is shyn- 55 yng in all beaulte and in right haboundaunt rychesses. This is that me lackyth. She beholdeth me amonge other whiles in her prayers. Hit may happen well that love may torne her herte for to make th'aliance of her and me. And what is this men saye that love hurteth no man but yf hit be be his eyen? Yf the eyen be 60 not made for to see, I shal saye that my desire shall happe well. Where am I? Wher I am, I put me oute. Where is my herte? Where is my desir? I wote never what I thynke, and my thought

[1] so of

may be abusion and myn abuse may well be reversid. Myn eyen
65 peraventure wene to see that they see not. Myn eres ymagyne to here and yet they ben deef. I finde my self in a grete playne and vayne ataynt and yet more in a superfluous errour more than ony man may have. For whan I see this lady more excellente than the other in beaute and richesses, reson telleth me that she is not
70 comen hether for me. And whan I beholde that she is allone wythoute men in my cyte, who shall agaynsaye my will? I shall requyre her to be my wif after that she hath don her devocion. And yf she accorde to my requeste my werke shal doo well, and yf she gaynsaye and withstande hit than I muste use force and
75 auctorite royall.'

Thus whan Neptune cam to thys conclucion, Meduse aroos fro her contemplacion and lokyd right fayr. Neptune wente to her and dide her reverence and after prayd her that she wold goo to his ryall palays for to refresshe her. Meduse thankyd hym of
80 his curtoisie and saide that she mighte not well tarye there at that tyme. Whan Neptune understood that she was in wyll to retorne wythoute to areste her in his hows ne in his cyte he was sore displaysid in his herte. Alleway he held manyer and drewe her aparte and said unto her changyng colour: 'Madame, I am sory
85 that ye reffuse to take pacience in my hows. I am Kinge of this cyte. The goddes have not gyven to me so moche happe that I have yet ony wif, ony lady or damoysell. Hit is so now happend that the goddes and fortune hath enspyred yow to come hether. Certes hit is so now that your right hye beaute hath[1] perisshid
90 the eye of my herte and hath made me so covoytous of yow that I gyve unto yow herte, body and goodes and alle that a lover may gyve unto his love and lady or ony king may gyve. Wherfore I pray yow that ye will descende unto my palays to the ende that I may have comynycacion more secretly there and telle unto yow
95 the right grete love that I have in yow.'

Anone as Meduse understood the requestes of the Kynge she began to frowne, and not wyllyng to be otherwyse she answerd to hym: 'Syre Kynge, yf hit were soo that myn herte desired acqueyntance and commynycacion of oon man more than of

[1] that

another, in trouthe yf I so fonde me I shold holde my self right 100
happy findyng my self in the grace of your eyen. But the mater
goth wyth me all otherwyse. I love the men as moche oon as
another. I have entencion to abyde and contynue in my virginite.
Ye be a kynge, ye have gyven to me saufconduyt to achyeve my
pylgrymage. I requyre yow that ye holde yow plesid and that ye 105
doo in suche wyse as ye had never seen me.'

'Dame,' sayde Neptune, 'how shall I doo that ye saye, whan
my herte is all gyven unto yow?'

'Syre,' answerd Meduse, 'hyt behoveth fyrst to knowe and
after that to love. I have told yow hyer that I have entencion to 110
abyde a virgyne. What may hit prouffite yow to saye that ye have
gyven me your herte? Thyse ben but loste wordes.'

'Dame,' sayd Neptune, 'the dyamond shyneth not tyl hit be
pollisshyd. Ye were never peraventure desired ne requyred of
love more than now, wherfore ye have no more love in oon man 115
than in another. Wherfore ye muste understand that the hauntyse
maketh love. And yf ye come wyth me and sojourne I make no
doubtes[1] that your wyll shall change and that ye shall take alyance
wyth me.'

'Syre,' answerd Meduse, 'my wyll is unchangeable.' 120

'Notwythstondyng,' sayd Neptune, 'hit muste change; and
abaysshe yow not.'

'Syre,' answerd Meduse, 'I see nothyng that yevyth me cause
of enbaysshement, for I fele my herte ferme and stable in his
operacions. Ye be a kynge and have gyven me saufconduyt for to 125
furnysh my devocion at the tepmle of the goddesse of your cyte.
Rayson and honour shold governe your corage.'

'Dame,' said Neptune, 'yf your beaute surmounted not the
beaute of other women, I shold consente anon your retorne. But
whan I conceyve yow formed in so hye degre of nature that 130
nothing lackyth in yow and further whan I see that the grete
goddesse Pallas hath enspyred yow to thys my cyte, rayson may
have no place. And how hit be by love or by force, ye shall be
my wif; for I had lever dye and renne into alle the deshonnours
of the world than for to faylle to have your allyance.' 135

[1] I make no doubtes and soiourne

Whan Meduse that was wise had understand the wordes of Neptune and sawe well that he was outragyously achauffid of her amorous desire and that she might not ascape his puyssance for her beaute but yf hit were by ony aventure, than she changed 140 her heer into coulevres, that is to saye that where force regned she wrought by subtilte, and said unto the Kynge: 'Syre, I knowe that ye be a grete and puyssant lord and that love hath mevyd yow by force to take me to your wif. Syn your playsir is suche, I am contente to do all in suche wyse as ye have demanded and 145 that this same day be maad the maryage of yow and me. But for more solempnly to halowe the feste of our espousailles I requyre yow of two thinges: first, that I may retorne unto the porte to my peple for to aray and dresse me with my triumphant richesses, for I ne may employe to more grete and glorie than this day of my 150 mariage; and secondly, that ye wyll do araye and adresse the ladyes of this cyte for to receyve me as hit apperteyneth. For I wyll well that ye knowe that in alle the remenant of ladyes of the world ye shall not finde ony that have more mevable goodes ne richesses than I have.'

155 Neptune was than as oon alle ravysshyd in joye whan he herde this answer of Meduse. He thankyd her of her swete wordes and agreed to her to do in suche wyse as she had devysed. And anon sente agayn this Meduse unto her galleyes hopyng that she wold retorne agayn to be his wyf. But whan she by the subtylte of her 160 wytte was rendred agayn at the porte where Neptune had no puyssance, in stede for to retorne to the cyte she dyde do disancre all her shippis and lete sayle falle and in all haste wythdrewe hem fro the porte. And in stede to aray her in vestementis nupciall she toke her armes and made all her men to arme them. And thus 165 she ascapyd from Neptune, whiche was in grete sorow merveyl-lously. And in grete anger sayde that she had hede of a serpent and that her heres were torned into coleuvers to the ende to hyde more graciously the malice of her and the manyer how she had deceyvyd and begyled hym.

170 Thus than ascaped Meduse the handes of Neptune by the meen of her hede serpentyne and Neptune abood convertyd and tornyd into stoone, that is to saye in erthely affections of richesses of

Meduse. And wente not after her for as moche as her puyssance surmountyd moche alle the puyssance of Atthenes. Of this thynge ran the renomee thurgh all Grece. And the beaute of Meduse 175 was so recomanded that of tho parties wente all daye many knightes aventuryng theyr lives. And many of them were torned into stones, and many loste theyr tresors innumerable enforcyng them by armes to conquere this lady whiche withstood alle way here assaultes and assayllyng and all way abode vainqueresse of 180 them. Meduse sette nowht by kynge ne prince that wold have her to wyf. She was alle sette to gete and gader the tresors of the world. Yf her fader had ben strongly coveytous, yet was she more covetous. And she comen agayn fro Athenes into her royame, after she had put under in subjection the Grekes that exposed 185 them ayenst her as said is, she so mountid into the depe swalowe of covetyse and avarice that she made warre unto alle her nyghe-bours and dauntyd hem and constraind them to paye her yerly grete tributes. Wherby her astate and name aroos and was so greet that the bruyt therof ran into many ferre regions and 190 amonge other into the cyte of Naples where regned the Kyng Pilonne, as afore is said.

In this tyme that the renomee of Meduse was in his bruyt, Perseus, sone of Danes and of Jupiter, was in the verdour of his begynnyng and tempryen strength, and dayly requyred his moder 195 and the Kinge that they wold gyve hym leve to serche hys aventures. Whan than Pylonnes herde speke of the haultesse of Meduse, of her rapines and of her avarice, he behelde that his sone-in-lawe shold do a vertuous werk yf he myght correcte her, told to Perseus that he wold sende hym theder. Perseus 200 thankyd hym and sayd he wold enploye therto all his puyssance. Than the Kynge Pylonne sente for men of armes and made redy thretty galeyes for th'exercyte of Perseus. Whan all was redy he callyd to hym on a day Perseus and dubbyd hym knyght, for the ordre of chevallrye began that tyme to be usid in all the 205 world. Hit was ordonned that that same day Perseus shold go to the see.

And whan the Kynge had accomplisshed all the serymonye to the caas requyred in the paynems wyse, Perseus toke leve of the

Kynge Pylonne and of his moder Danes and of the damoyselles and right joyously entryd into his galeye. After they dysancred and departyd fro the port of Naples wyth grete bruyt of tabours and trompes, and wyth banyer splayed saylyd into the hye see. Hit was a good and a fayr sight to see his departement. Ther was many a teer wept; everybody loved Perseus for so moche as he was humble and debonayr. The Apulyens departyd never as longe as they myghte see hym and than after they retorned home prayng unto the goddes that good and right happy myght be the fortune of Perseus.

And the noble knyght wente by the see and by the portes wythoute aventure. What shall I saye? He so exployted that he cam into Affrike, that was named Lybye at that tyme, and there wolde have refresshid hym at a port beside the Strayt of Gybalter, where as was Kynge Athlas, the grete astrologyen. But this Kynge put hym fro landyng at this porte and cam in armes ayenst hym and shewyd fro ferre signe that he wolde kepe his contre wyth the swerde. Than Perseus whyche wold not there employe his armee wythdrewe hym fro the porte en entencion to avenge hym another tyme of that rudesse, yf fortune wold helpe hym. He passid the strayte and sought so longe the royame of Meduse that anone after he fonde hit and had veray tydinges by certain marchantes, that he fonde labouryng on the see, that told hym that she and her susters sojourned in a cyte whiche stode on the ryvage.

Grete was the joye of Perseus whan he understood these tydinges. His folk had grete nede of vitayll. He callid hem all and saide that they shold make hem redy and arme them, for they were nyhe the place that they soughte. And than as they saylid alway forth, aboute thre owres tofore the even they sawe the cyte where Meduse was inne. And moreover they sawe Meduse and her susters with grete nombre of men of warre that renged them on the porte so richely arayed and in poynt, that hit was mervaylle to see. Whan Perseus sawe this he dyvydyd his armee in thre egale bataylles, eche of ten galeyes, and ordeyned and put in capitaynes of warre and wysely enformed hem how to nyhe and approche the porte. And after he put hym self in the first batayll.

And the poetes saye that the goddes Pallas gaf to hym than a shelde of cristall. That is to understande that he approuchyd right wysely the porte that was upon the grete see of Spayne; and that he conduyted hym self by suche prudence, that is likenyd to 250 cristall, that he cam and fought hand of hand the puyssance of Meduse; and that shynyng the ryght clere shelde of hys prudence in receyvyng and yevyng infinyte strokes he gate lande and constrayned Meduse to retorne into her cyte by force of armes and by prowesse and wyth grete dyscipline and fightyng of his sow- 255 dyours. At that tyme the hede of serpent of Meduse myght not wythstonde his firste fortunes. For she, that was acustomed to put under foot and overcome alle them that exposed them in armes ayenst her, at this tyme was put to th'extremyte where she had put other to. 260

Suche was the entre of the warre that was betwene Perseus and Meduse where the Gorgonnes fortunat, whiche Meduse had cherysshed in right hye degree,[1] fille doun fro the whele of fortune; whiche whele had consented that the prudence of Perseus sholde be cause of her humylieng and mekyng. This not- 265 wythstondyng Meduse took corage in her self and re-entryd into her cyte and gaf charge to oon of her men to go unto her enemyes and to enquere of them who was chief and captayn of hem and what thinge he soughte in her countre. The Hisperyen at comandement of Meduse departyd fro the cyte and cam to the 270 ooste of the Apuliens that entended for to logge them that nyght. He did so moche that he cam to Perseus that toke his refection upon a table that he had maad of a grete stoon of marbell and sayde to hym in this wyse. 'Syre, the vaynqueresse of men hath sente me to thee for to enquere what thyng thou wylt doo in her 275 contre to the ende that she may knowe what she hath to do.'

'Messanger,' answerd Perseus, 'I have entencion to fraunchise and make fre the men fro the servytude that thy maystresse holdeth hem in, and to make her that hath but oon eye that she converte and torne men no more into stones, and that her richesses 280 shall be no more the causes of the losse and perdicion of knyghtes whiche wold have her in mariage. For ayenst her malice of the

[1] degrce

serpente I shall be armed with prudence, and will wel that she knowe that to morn withoute lenger delaye I shal gyve assault
285 unto her cyte in caas she come not agaynst me in batayll.'

Sith this answere the Esperien retorned unto Meduse and recountyd unto her all that he had herd. Meduse assemblid than alle her men of warre and said to them: 'Hit is not mervaylle though I have myn herte anguysshous, whan after that I have vaynquys-
290 shyd grete companyes of men of armes that I see that shamefully we ben goon aback and withdrawen into this cyte by the prowesse of an handfull of men. O what anguysshe is this to them that have ben in custome to overcome and to tryumphe in alle maner warres. Where ben the hye enterprises by whiche we have made
295 alle the sees occidentall to fere and drede us? Where ben the glayves that had ben yolden to us of the kynges, our trybutaryes? Where ben the armes and strengthes that hath made to tremble the mountaygnes and roches of Libye? Where be they that this day have taken feer for prowesse, drede for hardynes, dishonour
300 for honour? At leste sin this thinge is so governed hit behoveth to passe the best wise we may. But now hit behoveth also that every man corage and vertue hym self, and that to morn hyt be recoveryd that by us thys day is loste. The enemyes of thys cyte have don us to understonde and knowe that to morn they wyll
305 gyve us assault, if we ne furnyssh them of bataylle. And how hit be also that they ben travayllyd of the ayer of the see, hit is moche better that we furnyssh them of bataylle at this tyme than we sholde abyde lenger. Oure enemyes ben straungers. Here lieth our triumphe or our mortall mysadventure. Yf we overcome
310 them hit shall be a memorye of us ferre and nyghe in all honour; yf the caas goo contrarye we shall renne wyth the losse of our lyves into derision and mocquerye of alle peples. And what is this? Shall the blood be spred abrood of them that have made the ground rede of the blood of other? Shalle the honour be wastyd
315 and loste and also the name that we have goten wyth so grete labour? Alle the world taketh courage and hope. These two thynges ben also covenable in warre as the armes, and wythoute them shall never man attayne to the crowne of victorye. A than, take herte to yow and dispose your harnoys and armes. To morn

shall be the day that ye muste nede do shyne your dedes the beste 320
wyse ye may and for to kepe your renomees and your tytles of honourable prowesse.'

'Dame,' answerd oon of ther capitayns, 'it is grete domage that ye ne were a man. For yf hit had be so, hit is so apparant that ye shold have subjuged and put under alle the monarchye of men. 325
As ye saye we muste nedes kepe oure renome. Yf fortune hath ben to us this day froward, to morn she shal torn to prouffyt. The woundes and hurtes that ben made in our worship and blood we moste bere hit and take hit in gree. And our prowesse and honour shall to morn putte us tofore the shame. We shall 330
esvertue us. Conne not ye ryse so erly that we myght be on the fronte of hem well arayed and apparaylid for to laboure for the prosperite of your requeste?'

Whan Meduse herde the good wille of her capitayne, to whom consentid all the other, she was right joyous, and concluded with 335
them that she with all her puissance shold bespringe and assayll her enemies at midnyght in hope to come upon hem unwares. This conclucion thought good unto alle. And eche man with-drewe for to take her reste and for to make redy his harnoys. Meduse slepte not moche this night as she that had the herte alway 340
grete and sore chargid with appetite of vengeance.

And at midnyght than she sowned to armes and made hem to be redy and adoubed. She toke her banyers that were right riche. Her men were diligent inowh to arme them for of that crafte they were well enduced. And whan they were redy and 345
assemblid tofore the palais riall, Meduse and her susters yssuid oute of the gate in riche astate. And gyvyng good morow to her folk with as litill noyse as she myght, she devidyd hem in two companyes. Wherof she made oon companye to departe by oon of the yates of the cyte and she her self conduyted that other by 350
the yate that was ayenste the porte or haven.

At this tyme the ayer was pure and net and the sterres twinklid and the mone shone and put away the derknes of the nyght acordyng to her celestyall offyce. Whan Meduse was in the feldes she wente after the ryvage of the see and supposid to have taken 355
Perseus and his folke, but she faylled. For as sone as she yssuyd out

of her cyte hit was parceyvyd of the wacchemen of the ooste of Perseus and they signefied theyr comyng to Perseus and hys men that slept in her harnoys. And thus whan she approchid unto her
360 enemyes and had supposid to have distressid them, she fonde them arayed and renged in good ordenance of bataylle. Wherof ther aroos a right grete crye of bothe parties. And wyth this crye ther engendryd a grete scarmuche so eygre and fiers that hit was nede unto alle to put forth her prowesses and theyr strengthes. There
365 was many man cast doun dede upon the sande. Ther was many a swerd dyed reed wyth blood. There cam on the seconde bataylle of Meduse makyng grete bruyt in joynnyng of the bataylle. And than had they of Naples stronge partye for to maystrye.

370 In this tempeste Perseus gafe hym to no reste. He had alway his eyen open, his eeres bent to here, his armes enhaunsed to smyte. He was quyk and in hys grene yongthe. His swerde trenchid and cutted dispairly. He smote no man ne shelde but he al tofrusshid hit and slewe doun right. Meduse that alway put her in the most
375 strength and frayes and moste prees by myghty grete corage for to entretene and to holde togeder her men, seeyng often tymes the appertisements and the noble fetes of armes of her enemy Perseus had grete sorowe. For his only conduyte helde the Apuliens in estate and aray; and ther was none that myghte resiste his
380 strength or at leste that had myght for to resiste hym. This thinge torned to grete displaysir to Meduse. Alleway she bare this displaysir and usid her prowesse the beste wyse she myghte. She dyde grete domage to her enemyes and smote doun here and there so vaylliantly that she semed moche better to be a man than
385 a woman; and better became her to brandissh a swerde than to spynne or torne a spyndell. This scarmuche than dured longe with grete betyng doun of men of armes and of knyghtes. Th'envye that Meduse had of well doyng of Perseus gaf to her armes more force and strength than[1] nature had gyven her. She
390 was full of malice. And she coude kepe her well fro the swerd of Perseus and all way she was envyronned of the best men she had.

[1] that

What shall I make longe counte? They fought in this facion unto the day withoute that ony wyste to whom me shold gyve the victorye. But than like as the sonne began to sprede and shewe 395 his bemes and rayes, in semblable wise Perseus began to shewe the rayes of his prudence and braundisshid his swerd. And seeyng on that oon side the banyer royall, he smote into the prees and drewe to that parte castyng men doun dede on the sandes moo than an honderd. This banyer was square four foot made of 400 cremesin satin, and in the myddes was an ymage paintyd wherof the body was a figure and facion of a woman and the hede was of a serpente. Meduse was never ferre fro thys banyer for as moche as she drewe her allwey theder to for rescuse. Whan Perseus was comen theder with grete sute of hys folk he cryed 'Perseus, 405 Perseus'. And liftyng his swerd that was temprid with blood from on ende to that other, hit happend that the first strook that he gaf in this place fille upon oon of the susters of Meduse so terribly that she confounded ded wyth a grete wounde begynnyng on her heed doun to her stomack. Than they of Naples smote on the 410 Hesperyens with alle her puyssance. Tho smote Perseus endlong and overthwart on the right side and on the lefte side. His strokes were so mortall that they affrayed not only the most feble of his enemyes but alle the most strengest and also the asseured Meduse. Grete was the occision. 415

In this point Meduse enforced her power to wythstonde the grete force of Perseus. This notwythstandyng she that afore tymes had overcomen the men was than overcomen. And havyng late the corage lifte up and the herte more fiers than ony man, she was veynquysshid of despayr for the only chevaulrous conduyte of 420 Perseus that had broken her banyer, that had smyten her men in pieces, partye slayn wyth his swerd and partye fled, and that he had not only made reed his swerd and right hand wyth her blood but the see by smale goters was made rede of the warm blood, in whiche Meduse lost her ferocyte, alle her presumpcion, alle her 425 strength and alle her vigour. So evyll wente and alle the werke on her side that whan she had seen her banyer destroyed, whan she had seen the moste victoryous of her knightes confounded by tempest of deth, whan she sawe her men of armes leve the bataylle

430 and flee tofore Perseus as tofore the ymage of deth, fynably she sawe alle her puysance torne into destruction generall. Wherof the ende was that eche man gaf hit over and every man that myght save hym self savyd hym by caves and busshes, here oon and there another, so sore affrayed that hit was a pietous thing to here 435 theyr cryes. And many savyd them in the cyte and many were slayn in the fleyng of Perseus and his men.

Perseus at thys disconfiture poursued Meduse fleyng into her cyte and entryd in with her and the moste parte of his peple with hym. That faylid hym never to put to deth alle the men defens- 440 able that they fonde to th'ende that no insurrection shold be ayenst them. But they spared the blood of women and lityll children by the comandement of Perseus. And amonge the other as Perseus had founde Meduse that was put in a cisterne, he had pytye of her. How be hit he smote of her hede in suche facion 445 that the blood that yssuyd out engendrid Pegasus, the fleyng hors.

By the hede that Perseus smote of of Meduse is understond that he toke from her her royame and depryvyd her of hit and ban- nysshid her poure and nakyd. And by the fleyng hors that was engendrid of the blood yssued fro her hede is understande that of 450 her richesses issuyng of that royame he founded and made a shippe named Pegase, that is as moche to saye as good renomee. And this shippe was likened unto an hors fleyng for as moche as the good renomee of Perseus was than born fro region to region in suche wise as upon an hors fleing, and for as moche as Perseus 455 wente in this shippe in dyverce contrees where he gate hym a grete name.

Bi this facion than Perseus conquerd the hede of Meduse and did do make Pegase the most swyft shyppe that was in alle the world. And abode there certayn nombre of dayes seekyng and 460 serching the tresours of Meduse and the rychesses in whiche she and her susters had sette her entencion and her herte. There fonde Perseus stones precyous and thinges mervayllous. Whan his shippe was made, he filde hit with precyous bagues and juellis. And levyng in this cyte men for to governe hit and conduyte, he 465 wente to the see and toke for his armes the armes of Meduse.

XI. Æsop's Fables

(a) *The banking of money*

A SPAYNARD arryved somtyme into the lande of Egipte and bycause that he doubted to be robbed within the desertys of Arabé, he purposed and bethought in hym self that it were wysely done to take his money to somme trewe man for to kepe hit unto his retorne ageyne. And bycause that he herd somme 5 saye that within the cyte was a trewe man, he anone wente to hym and toke to hym his sylver for to kepe hit. And whan he had done his vyage, he came ageyne to hym and demaunded of hym his sylver. Whiche ansuerd to hym in this manere: 'My frend, I ne wote who thow arte for I sawe the never that I wote 10 of. And yf thou sayest or spekest ony more wordes I shalle make the to be wel bete.'

Thenne was the Spaynard sorowful and wroth, and therof he wold have made a playnte to his neyghbours; as he dyde. And the neyghbours sayd to hym: 'Certaynly we be wel abasshed of 15 that that ye telle to us, for he is emonge us alle reputed and holden for a good man and trewe. And therfore retorne ageyne to hym and by swete wordes telle hym that he wyl rendre to the thy good ageyne.' The whiche thynge he dyd; and the old man ansuerd to hym more sharply and rygorously than he had done before. 20 Wherof the Spaynard was wonderly wrothe.

And as he departed oute of the old mans hows, he mette with an old woman, the whiche demaunded of hym wherfore he was soo troubled and hevy. And after that he had told to her the cause why, th'old woman sayd to hym: 'Make good chere, for yf hit be 25 so as thow sayst I shalle counceylle the how thow shalt recovere thy sylver.' And thenne he demaunded of her how hit myght be done. And she sayd to hym: 'Bryng hyther to me a man of thy countrey whome thow trustest, and doo to be made four fayr chestes and fylle them alle with stones. And by thy felawes thow shalt make 30 them to be borne into his hows, and to hym they shalle say that the marchaunts of Spayne send them to hym for to be kepte surely. And whan the chestes shalle be within his hows, thow

shalt go and demande of hym thy sylver.' Whiche thynge
35 he dyd.

And as the sayd chestes were borne within his hows, the Spaynard wente with them that bare them. The whiche straungers sayd to the old man: 'My lord, these four chestes ben al ful of gold, of sylver and of precious stones, whiche we brynge to yow
40 as to the trewest man and feythful that we knowe for to kepe them surely bycause that we fere and doubte the theves whiche ben within the desert.' After the whiche wordes sayd, came he whiche the old woman had counceylled and demaunded of hym his sylver. And bycause that the old man doubted that the
45 Spaynard wold have dispreysed hym, he sayd thus to hym: 'Thow arte welcome. I merveylled how thow taryest soo longe for to come.' And incontynent he restored to hym his sylver. And thus by the counceylle of the woman, whiche he gretely thanked, he had his good ageyn and retourned ageyne into his countrey.

(*b*) *Woman's subtlety*

THE cautele or falshede of the woman is wonder merveyllous as it appiereth by this fable of a marchaunt whiche was wedded of newe unto a fayre and yong woman. The whiche marchaunt wente over the see for to bye and selle and for to gete somwhat
5 for to lyve honestly. And bycause that he dwellyd to longe his wyf supposed that he was dede. And therfore she enamoured her self with another man, whiche dyd to her mykle good as for to have doo make and bylde up his hows of newe, the whiche had grete nede of reparacion. And also he gaf to her all newe utensyles
10 to kepe a houshold. And within a long tyme after the departyng of the marchaunt he came ageyne into his hows whiche he sawe newe bylded and sawe dysshes, pottes, pannes and suche other houshold [utensyles]. Wherfore he demaunded of his wyf how and in what manere she had founde the facion and the meane for
15 to have repayred so honestly his hows. And she ansuerd that it was by the grace of God. And he ansuerd: 'Blessyd be God of hit.' And when he was within the chambre he sawe the bedde rychely coverd and the walles wel hanged and demaunded of his

wyf [as] he had done before. And she thenne ansuerd to hym in lyke maner as she dyd before. And therfore he thanked God as he had done tofore. And as he wold sette hym at his dyner, there was brought before hym unto his wyf a child of thre yere of age or thereaboute. Wherfore he demaunded of his wyf: 'My frend, to whome belongeth this fayre child?' And she ansuerd: 'My frend, the Holy Ghoost of his grace hath sente hit to me.' Thenne ansuerd the marchaunt to his wyf in this manere: 'I rendre not graces ne thankes not to the Holy Ghoost of this, for he hath taken to moche payne and labour for to have it made up myn owne werke. And I wyll that in no maner wyse he medle no more therwith, for suche thynge belongeth to me for to doo hit and not to the Holy Ghoost.'

(*c*) *The dean and the parish priest*

Now thenne I wylle fynysshe alle these fables wyth this tale that foloweth whiche a worshipful preest and a parsone told me late. He sayd that there were duellynge in Oxenford two prestes, bothe maystres of arte, of whome that one was quyck and coude putte hym self forth and that other was a good symple preest. And soo it happed that the mayster that was perte and quyck was anone promoted to a benefyce or tweyne and after to prebendys and for to be a dene of a grete prynces chappel, supposynge and wenynge that his felaw the symple preest shold never have be promoted but be alwey an annuel or at the most a parysshe preest. So after longe tyme [it happed] that this worshipful man, this Dene, came rydynge into a good paryssh with a x or xij horses lyke a prelate and came into the chirche of the sayd parysshe and fond there this good symple man, somtyme his felawe, whiche cam and welcomed hym lowely.

And that other badde hym 'Good morowe, Mayster Johan', and toke hym sleyghtly by the hand and axyd hym where he dwellyd. And the good man sayd: 'In this paryssh.'

'How,' sayd he, 'are ye here a sowle preest or a paryssh preste?'

'Nay, syr,' said he, 'for lack of a better, though I be not able ne worthy, I am parson and curate of this parysshe.'

And thenne that other avaled his bonet and said: 'Mayster parson, I praye yow to be not displeasyd; I had supposed ye had 25 not be benefyced. But, mayster,' sayd he, 'I pray yow what is this benefyce worth to yow a yere?'

'Forsothe,' sayd the good symple man, 'I wote never for I make never accomptes therof, how wel I have had hit four or fyve yere.'

30 'And knowe ye not,' said he, 'what it is worth? It shold seme a good benefyce.'

'No, forsothe,' sayd he, 'but I wote wel what it shalle be worth to me.'

'Why,' sayd he, 'what shalle hit be worth?'

35 'Forsothe,' sayd he, 'yf I doo my trewe dylygence in the cure of my parysshens in prechyng and techynge and doo my parte longynge to my cure, I shalle have heven therfore. And yf theyre sowles ben lost or ony of them by my defawte, I shall be punysshed therfore. And herof am I sure.'

40 And with that word the ryche dene was abasshed and thought he shold be the better and take more hede to his cures and benefyces than he had done. This was a good answere of a good preest and an honest.

XII. Game and Play of the Chess (1475)

Taverners and the vice of gluttony

THE sixthe pawn whiche standeth tofore the alphyn on the lyfte syde is made in thys forme, for hit is a man that hath the right hande stracched oute as for to calle men and holdeth in his lyfte hande a loof of breed and a cuppe of wyn and on his gurdell 5 hangynge a bondell of keyes. And this resembleth the taverners, hostelers and sellars of vitaylle. And thise ought proprely to be sette tofore the alphyn as tofore a juge, for ther sourdeth ofte tymes amonge hem contencion, noyse and stryf whiche behoveth to be determyned and trayted by the alphyn whiche is juge of the 10 kynge. And hit apperteyneth to them for to seke and enquyre for good wyns and good vitayll for to gyve and selle to the byers and to them that they herberowe. And hit apperteyneth to them well to kepe their herberowes and innes and alle tho thyngis that they brynge into theyr loggynge and for to putte hyt in seure and sauf warde and kepynge. And the firste of them is signefyed by the 15 lyfte hande in whiche he bereth brede and wyn. And the seconde is signefied by the right hande whiche is stracched oute to calle men. And the thirde is representid by the keyes hangynge on the gurdell.

And thyse maner of peple ought t'eschewe the synne of 20 glotonye, for moche peple comen into theyr howses for to drynke and to ete. For whyche cause they ought resonably to rewle them self and to refrayne them from to moche mete and drynke to th'ende that they myght the more honestly delyvere thyngis nedefull unto the peple that come unto them and nothynge by 25 oultrage that myght noye the body. For hit happeth ofte tymes that ther cometh of glotonye tencyons, stryfs, ryottes, wronges and molestacyons by whiche men lese other while their handes, theyr eyen and other of their membres, and somtyme ben slayn or hurt unto the deth. As it is wreton in *Vitas Patrum* as on a tyme 30 an heremyte wente for to visite his gossibs. And the devyll apperyd to hym on the waye in lykenes of another heremyte for to tempte hym and saide: 'Thou hast lefte thyn heremitage and goost to visyte thy gossibs. The behoveth by force to doo one of the thre thynges that I shall saye to the. Thou shalt chese 35 whether thou wylt be dronke or ellys have to do flessly wyth thy gossib or ellys thou shalt sle her husbond whiche is thy gossip also.' And the hermyte that thought for to chese the leste evyll chace for to be dronke. And whan he cam unto them he dranke so moche that he was veray dronke. And whan he was dronke 40 and eschauffed wyth the wyn, he wold have adoo wyth hys gossib. And her husbonde wythstode hym; and than the hermyte slewe hym. And after that laye by his gossib and knewe her flessly. And thus by this synne of dronkenship he accomplisshid the two other synnes. 45

By whyche thynge ye may understande and knowe that whan the devyll wyll take one of the castellis of Jhesu Cryst, that is to wete the body of a man or of a woman, he doth as a prynce that setteth a siege tofore a castell that he wold wynne, whiche 50 entendeth to wynne the gate. For he knoweth well whan he hath wonne the gate he may sone doo hys wylle wyth the castell. And in lyke wyse doth the devyll wyth every man and woman. For whan he hath wonne the gate, that is to wete the gate of the mouth, by glotonye or by other synne, he may doo wyth the 55 offices of the body alle his wylle as ye have herd tofore. And therfore ought every man ete and drynke sobrely in suche wyse as he may lyve, and not lyve to ete glotonsly and for to drynke dronke. Ye see comunly that a grete bole is suffisid wyth right a lityll pasture and that a wode suffiseth to many olefauntes. And 60 hit behoveth a man to be fedde by the erthe or by the see. Nevertheles, it is no grete thynge to fede the bely, nothynge so grete as is the desire of many metes.

Wherof Quyntylian sayth that hit happeth ofte tymes in grete festes and dyners that we be fylde wyth the sight of the noble and 65 lichorous metis, and whan we wolde ete we ben saciat and fild. And therfore hit is sayd in proverbe: hit is better to fylle the bely than the eye. And Lucan sayth the glotonye is the moder of alle vices and especiall of lecherye, and also is destroyer of all goodes and may not have suffisance of lityll thynge. A covetous honger, 70 what sekest thou mete and vitayllis on the lande and in the see? And thy joye is nothynge ellis but to have playnteuous disshes and well fylde at thy table. Lerne how men may demene his lyf wyth lityll thynge. And Cathon sayth, in no wyse obeye to glotonye whiche is frende to lecherye. And the holy doctour 75 Saynt Augustyn sayth, the wyn eschauffeth the bely that falleth anone to lecherye. The bely and the membrers engendreurs ben neyghebours to lecherye. And thus the vice of glotonye provoketh lecherye wherof cometh forgetenes of his mynde and destruction of alle quyk and sharp reson, and is cause of distemperance of his 80 wittes. What synne is fowler than this synne and more stynkynge ne more domageous, for this synne hath taken away the vertue of the man? His prowesse languissheth,[1] his vertue is torned to diffame, the strengthe of body and of corage is torned by the.

[1] languisshed

And therfore sayth Basille le grant, late us take hede how we serve the bely and the throte by glotonye lyke as we were dombe bestes. 85 And we studye for to be lyke unto belues of the see to whom nature hath gyven to be alleway enclined toward the erthe and ther to loke for to serve theyr belyes. And herof saith Boecius *De Consolacione* in his fourth book that a man that lyvyth and doth not the condicions of a man may never be in good condicion; 90 than muste hit nedes be that he be transported in nature of a beste or of a belue of the see. How well that ryght grete men and women full of mervayllous sciences and noble counceyll in thise dayes in the world ben kept and nourisshid in this glotonye of wyns and metes and ofte tymes ben overseen, how suppose ye, 95 is hit not right a perillous thinge that a lord or governour of the peple and commun wele, how well that he be wyse, yf he eschauffe hym sone so that the wyn or other drynke surpryse hym and overcome his brayn? His wysedom is loste. For as Cathon sayth, ire enpessheth the corage in suche as he may not kepe verite 100 and trouthe, and anon as he is chauffed lecherye is mevyd in hym in suche wyse that the lecherye maketh hym to medle in dyverse villayns dedes, for than his wysedom is aslepe and goon. And therfore sayth Ovide in his booke *De Remedio Amoris*, yf thou take many and dyverce wyns they apparylle and enforce the 105 corages to lecherye. And Thobie witnessith in his booke that luxurye destroyeth the body and mynussheth richesses, she loseth the sowle, she febleth the strengthe, she blyndeth the syght and maketh the voys hoos and rawe.

Ha a, ryght evyll and fowle synne of dronkenship, by the 110 perissheth virginite whiche is suster of angellis, possedynge alle goodnes and seurte of alle joyes pardurable. Noe was one tyme so chauffed with wyn that he discoverd and shewid to his sones his prevy membres in suche wyse as one of his sones mocqued hym and that other coverd hem. And Loth whiche was a man 115 right chaste was so assoted by moche drynkynge of wyn that on a montayne he knewe his doughters carnelly and had to doo wyth them as they had ben his propre wyves. And Boece[1] reherceth that Crete[2] whiche was flour of the men, tresor of

[1] Crete [2] Boece

120 rychesses, singuler house of sapience, myrour of the world, odour of good renome and glorye of his subgettis, loste alle thyse thynges by his luxurye. We have seen that dyverce that were joyned by grete amyte togeder whiles they were sobre that that one wolde put his body in paryll of deth for that other, and whan
125 they were eschauffed with wyn and dronke they have ronne eche upon other for to sle hem. And somme have ben that have slayn so his frende. Herodes Antipas had not doon Saynt Johan Baptist to ben beheded ne had the dyner ben full of glotonye and dronkenship. Balthazar, Kynge of Babilone, had not ben chaced
130 out of his kyngdom ne be slayn yf he had ben sobre amonge his peple, whom Tyrus and Dares fonde dronken and slewe hym.

The hostelers ought to be well bespoken and courtoys of wordes to them that they receyve into their loggynge, for fayr speche and joyous chiere and debonayr cause men to gyve the
135 hostelyer a good name. And therfore it is said in a comyn proverbe, courtoyse langage and wellsaynge is moche worth and coste lityll. And in another place it is said that curtoysie passeth beaulte. Also for as moche as many paryls and adventures may happen on the wayes and passages to hem that ben herbe-
140 rowed within their innes, therfore they ought to accompanye them whan they departe and enseigne them the wayes and telle to them the paryls to th'ende that they may surely goo theyr viage and journey. And also they ought to kepe their bodies, their goodes and the good fame and renomee of their innes. We
145 rede that Loth whan he had receyvyd the angels into his hous right debonairly whiche he had supposid had ben mortall men and straungers, to th'ende that they shold eskape the disordinate and unnaturell synne of lecherye of the Sodamites, by the vertu of good fayth he sette apart the naturell love of a fader and proferd to
150 them his doughters whiche were virgyns to th'ende that they shold kepe them and defende them fro that vyllayne and horrible synne.

And knowe ye for certayn that alle tho thynges that ben taken and delyveryd to kepe to the hoste or hostesses, they ought to be sauf and yelden agayn wythout apayringe. For the ooste ought
155 to knowe who that entryth into his hous for to be herberowhed taketh hit for his habitacion for the tyme. He hym self and alle

suche thynges as he bryngeth wyth hym ben commysed of ryght in the warde and kepynge of the hoost or hosteler, and ought to be as sauf as they were put in his owen propre hous. And also suche hoostis ought to hold servantes in their houses whiche 160 shold be trewe and wythoute avarice in suche wise that they coveyte not to have the goodes of their ghestes, and that they take not away the provender fro theyr horses whan hyt is gyven to them that by th'occasion therof theyr horsis perisshe not ne faylle theyr maister whan they have nede and myght falle in the 165 handes of theyr enemyes. For than sholde the servantes be cause of that evyll, wherfore theyr maisters shold see to. For wythoute doubte this thynge is worse than thefte. Hit happend on a tyme in the parties of Lomberdye in the cyte of Jene that a noble man was logged in an hostelerye wyth moche compaignye. And whan 170 they had gyven provendour to their horses, in the first oure of the nyght the servant of the hous cam secretly tofore the horses for to stele away their provender. And whan he cam to the lordes hors, the hors caught wyth his teth his arme and helde hit faste that he myght not escape. And whan the theef sawe that he was 175 so strongly holden, he began to crye for the grete payne that he suffryd and felte in suche wyse that the noble mannes meyne cam with the hooste. But in no maner ner for ought they coude doo, they coude not take the theef out of the horses mouth unto the tyme that the neyghbours whiche were noyed wyth the noyse 180 cam and sawe hit. And than the theef was knowen and taken and brought tofore the juge and confessid the feet and by sentence diffinytyf was hanged and lost his lyf. And in the same wyse was another that dyde so and the hors smote hym in the visage that the prynte of the horseshoo and nayles abode ever in his visage. 185

Another caas right cruell and villaynous fylle at Tholouse. Hit happend a ionge man and his fader wente a pilgremage to Saynt James in Galyce; and were logged in an hostelrye of an evyll hoost and full of right grete covetyse, in so moche that he desired and coveyted the goodes of the two pilgrimes. And hereupon 190 avysed hym and put a cuppe of silver secretly in the male that the yonge man bare. And whan they departed oute of their loggynge, he folowed after hem and sayd tofore the peple of the court that

they had stolen and born away his cuppe. And the yonge man
195 excused hym self and his fader and sayde they were innocent of
that caas. And than they serchid hem and the cuppe was founden
in the male of the yonge man, and forthwyth he was dampned to
the deth and hanged as a theef. And this feet doon, all the goodes
that langed to the pilgrym were deliverid to the oost as confisqued.
200 And than the fader wente for to do his pilgremage. And whan he
cam agayn, he muste nedes come and passe by the place where
his sone henge on the gibet. And as he cam he complaygned to
God and to Saynt James how they might suffre this aventure to
come unto his sone. Anone his sone that henge spack to his fader and
205 sayde how that Saynt James had kepte hym without harme and
bad his fader goo to the juge and shewe to hym the myracle
and how he was innocent of that fayte. And whan this thynge was
knowen the sone of the pilgryme was taken doun fro the gibet,
and the cause was brought tofore the juge. And the hooste was
210 accused of the trayson and he confessid his trespaas and sayd he
dide hit for covetyse to have his good. And than the juge dampned
hym for to be hanged on the same gibet where as the yonge
pilgryme was hanged.

And that I have sayd of the servantes beynge men, the same
215 I saye of the women, as chambriers and tapsters. For semblable
caas fille in Spayne at Saynt Donne of a chamberier that put a
cup in lyke wyse in the scrippe of a pilgryme because he wold not
have adoo wyth her in the synne of lecherye. Wherfore he was
hanged. And his fader and moder that were there with hym wente
220 and dyde her pilgremage. And whan they cam agayn they fonde
her sone lyvynge. And than they wente and told the juge, whiche
juge sayd that he wolde not byleve hit tyll a cok and an henne
whiche rosted on the fyre were alyve and the cok crewe. And anon
they began wexe alyve and the cok crewe and began to crowe and
225 to pasture. And whan the juge sawe this miracle, he wente and
toke doun the sone and made the chamberyer to be taken and to
be hanged. Wherfore I saye that the hoostes ought to hold no
tapsters ne chamberyers but yf they were good, meure and
honeste, for many harmes may befalle and come by the disorde-
230 nat rewle of servantes.

XIII. Mirror of the World (1481)

The exploits of Virgil

VIRGYLE, the wyse philosophre born in Itaile, was tofore the comyng of Our Lord Jhesu Cryst. He sette not lytil by the vij sciences, for he travaylled and studyed in them the most part of his tyme so moche that by astronomye he made many grete mervaylles. For he made in Naples a flye of copper, whiche whan he had sette it up in a place that flye enchaced and hunted away alle other flyes so that ther myght abyde none in ony place ne durste none approche nyghe to that flye by the space of two boweshote round aboute. And yf ony flye passed the bounde that Virgyle had compassed, incontynent it shold deye and myght no lenger lyve. He made also an hors of brasse, the whiche guarisshed and heled alle horses of all their maladyes and seknesses of whiche they were entechid also sone as the seke hors loked on the hors of brasse. Also he founded a mervayllous cyte upon an egge by suche force and power that whan the egge was mevyd all the cyte quaved and shoke; and the more the egge was mevyd the more the cyte quaved and trembled. The cyte in hye and lowe and in playn, the flye of copper and hors of brasse that Virgyle thus made ben in Naples and the cage where the egge is in; alle ben there seen. This hath be sayd to us of them that be comen fro thens and that many tymes have seen them.

Also he made that in one day alle the fyre thurghout Rome faylled and was quenchid in suche wise that no persone myght have none but yf he wente and fette it at the nature of a woman with a candel or otherwyse. And she was doughter of th'Emperour and a grete lady whiche tofore had don to hym a grete sklaundre and dysplaysir. And all they that had fette fyre at her myght not adresse it to other, but everych that wolde have fyre muste nedes go fetche it there as the other had fette it. And thus avenged he hym on her for the displaysir that she had don to hym.

And he made a brygge upon a water, the grettest that ever was made in the worlde, and is not knowen of what mater it is made,

whether it be of stone or of wode. But ther was never werkman
35 so subtyl ne carpenter ne mason ne other that coude so moche
knowe ne enserche wythin th'erthe ne wythin the water that they
myght knowe and fynde how that brygge was there sette ne how
it was susteyned in no maner ne atte endes ne in the myddys. And
men passed over frely and all wythout lettyng.

40 He made also a gardyn all aboute round closyd wyth th'ayer
wythout ony other closure, whiche was as thycke as a clowde.
And this gardyn was right hye fro th'erthe.

He made also two tapres and a lampe alyght and brennyng in
suche wise that it contynuelly brennyd wythout quenchyng and
45 mynusshed ne lassed nothyng. Thise thre thinges he enclosed
within th'erthe in suche wyse that no man can fynde it for all the
craft they can doo.

Yet made he an heed to speke which answerd of alle that
whiche he was demanded of and of that whiche shold happen and
50 come in th'erthe. So on a day he demanded of the heed how he
shold doo in a certayn werke where as he shold goo unto. But
the heed answerd to hym in suche wyse that he understode it not
wel, for hit sayde that yf he kept wel the heed he shold come
agayn all hole. And with this answere he wente his way wel as-
55 sured. But the sonne whiche that day gaf grete hete smote hym
on the hede and chauffed his brayn, of whiche he toke none hede,
that he gate therby a sekenes and maladye wherof he deyde. For
whan he had the answere of the heed he understode not that he
spack of his heed, but understode of the heed that spack to hym.
60 But it had be better that he had kept wel his owne heed. And
whan he felte hym self agrevyd wyth sekenesse, he made hym to
be born out of Rome for to be beryed in a castel beyng toward
Sezyle and a myle nyghe to the see. Yet ben there his bones whiche
ben better kept than others ben. And whan the bones of hym ben
65 remevyd the see begynneth to encreace and swelle so gretly that it
cometh to the castel. And the hyer they be reysed up, the hyer
groweth the see in suche wyse that the castel shold be drowned
yf they were not anon remysed and sette in their place. But thenne
whan they be sette agayn in their place, anon the see avaleth and
70 gooth away there as it was tofore. And this hath be oftymes

proved. And yet endure the vertues of hym, as they saye that have ben there.

Virgyle was a moche sage and subtyl clerke and ful of grete engyne, for unto his power he wold preve all the usages of clerkes as moche as was possible for hym to knowe. He was a man of 75 lytil stature; a lytil courbed was he on the back by right nature, and wente his heede hangyng doun and beholdyng the ground. Virgyle dyde and made many grete mervaylles whiche the herers shold holde for lesynges yf they herde them recounted, for they wolde not byleve that another coude doo suche thynge as they 80 coude not medle wyth. And whan they here speke of suche maters or of other that they see at their eyen and that they can not understonde ne knowe not therof, anon they saye that it is by th'elpe of the fende that werketh in suche maner, as they that gladly myssaye of peple of recommendacion, and also saye it is 85 good not to conne suche thynges. But yf they knewe the science and manere, they wold holde it for a moche noble and right werke of nature and without ony other espece of evyll. And whan they knowe not ne understonde the thinge they saye moche more evyl than well. 90

Certaynly who that knewe well astronomye ther is nothyng in the world of whiche he coude enquyre by reson but he shold have knowleche therof. And many thynges shold he doo that sholde seme myracles to the peple whiche that knewe nothynge of the science. I saye not but ther myght be wel don evyll by hym 95 that coude it, for ther is none so good science but that myght be entended therin somme malyce and that he myght use it in evyll that wolde so applye hym therto. God made never so good a gospel but somme myghte torne it contrarye to trouthe. And ther is nothynge so true but somme myght so glose that it shold 100 be to his dampnacion, who that wolde payne hym to do evyll, how wel it is no maystrye to do yll. Every man hath the power to drawe hym self to do well or to doo evyll, whiche that he wylle, as he that hath fre liberte of that one and of that other. Yf he gyve hym self to vertues this goodnes cometh to hym fro Our Lord. 105 And yf he be inclyned to doo evyll that bryngeth hym at th'ende to sorow and to payne perpetuell. Never shal the evyl-disposed man saye well of that he can not wel understonde and knowe. Ther is no craft, arte, ne scyence but it is good to be knowen whan 110 a man wyll gyve and applye hym self therto. But late hym doo nothyng ayenst God by whiche he lese his grace.

Alle thynge is knowen by astronomye sauf suche thynge as God wylle that it be not knowen. And so it is better to lerne that than to lerne to amasse and gadre togydre grete tresours. For who 115 that coude astronomye proprely he shold have all that he wold have on erthe, for hym shold faylle nothyng what somever he wold and yet more. But they had lever have the monoye. And they knowe not that it is of astronomye ne wherfore monoye was founden, how wel that they applye all their entendement for 120 to have it. But they retche not for to lerne sauf that whiche they knowe shal redounde to their singuler prouffyt.

XIV. **Book of the Knight of the Tower** (1484)

(*a*) *Wives ought to be obedient to their husbands*

AFTER this a woman in no maner wyse ought stryve ageynst her husbond ne answere hym so that he take therby displaysyre, lyke as dyde the wyf of a burgeys whiche answerd to her husbond so noiously and shamefully tofore the peple that he bicam angry 5 and felle to see hym self so rewlyd tofore the peple that he had therof shame. And he said to her and bad her ones or twyes that she shold be stylle and leve, but she wold not. And her husbond whiche was wrothe smote her with his fyste to the erthe, and smote her with his foote on the vysage so that he brake her nose, 10 by whiche she was ever after al disfygured. And soo by her ryotte and ennoye she gate her a croked nose moche evyll. It had ben moche better for her that she had holden her stylle and hadde suffred. Yet it is reson and ryght that the husbonde have the hyhe wordes, and it is but honoure to a good woman to suffre and 15 holde her in pees and leve the haultayn langage to her husbond and lord. And also it is in the contrarye to a woman grete shame and vylonye to stryve ageynst her husbond, be it wrong or right, and in especial tofore the peple. I say not but when she shall fynd hym alone and tyme but that she may wel reprehende hym and advyse hym in shewyng curtoysly that he had wrong and unright with hym. And yf he be a man resonable he shal conne her thanke. And yf he be other, yet hath not she done but her parte. For right so shold a wyse woman do by th'ensample of the wyse Quene Hester, wyf of the Kyng Assuere, whiche was moche melancolyque and hasty. But the good lady answerd not to his yre. But after when she sawe hym well attempryd, place and tyme, thenne dyde she what she wold. And it was grete wysedom of a woman. And thus ought wyse wymmen to do. By this ensample the wymmen that ben chydars and rampynge ben not of suche obeysaunce as was a wyf of a marchaunt of whome I shall saye and telle to yow.

In a tyme it happed that marchauntes of Fraunce cam from certayn fayres where as they sought draperye. And as they cam with marchaundyse fro Roan that one of them said: 'It is a moche fayre thynge a man to have a wif obeysaunt in alle thynges to her husbond. Verayly,' sayde that one, 'my wyf obeyeth me well.'

And the second said: 'I trowe that my wyf obeye[th] me better.'

'Ye,' sayd the thyrd, 'lete laye a wager that whiche wyf of us thre that obeyeth best her husbond and doeth sonnest his commaundement that he wynne the wager.' Wherupon they waged a jewele and accorded al thre to the same and sworen that none shold advertyse his wyf of this bargayn sauf only to saye to her 'Doo that whiche I shall commaunde what somever it be'.

After when they cam to the first mans hows, he sayd to his wyf: 'Sprynge into this bacyne.'

And she answerd: 'Wherfore or what nede is it?'

And he said: 'Bycause it playsyth me so and I wyll that thou do so.'

'Truly,' said she, 'I shall knowe fyrst wherfor I shal sprynge.' And soo she wold not doo it. And her husbond waxe moche angry and felle, and gafe her a buffet.

After thys they cam to the second marchauntes hows and he saide to his wyf lyke as that other saide that she wold doo his

55 commaundement. And it was not long after that he said to her: 'Sprynge into the basyn.' And she demaunded hym wherfore. And at the last ende for ought that he dyde, she dyd it not. Wherfore she was beten as that other was.

Thenne cam they to the thyrd mans hous, and there was the 60 table covered and mete set theron. And the marchaunt said to th'other marchauntes in theyr eres that after dyner he wold commaunde her to sprynge into the bacyn. And the husbond said to his wyf that what somever he commaunded her she shold do it. His wyf whiche that moche lovyd hym and dred hym herd wel 65 the word. And it was so that they bygan to ete, and there was no salt upon the table. And the goodman sayd to his wyf: 'Sail sur table.' And the goodwyf whiche hadde fere to disobeye hym sprang upon the table and overthrewe table, mete, wyn and platers to the ground.

70 'How,' said the goodman, 'is this the manere? Conne ye none other playe but this? Are ye mad or oute of youre wyt?'

'Syre,' said she, 'I have done youre commaundement. Have ye not said that youre commaundement shold be done what somever it was? Certaynly I have it done to my power how be it that 75 it is youre harme and hurte as moche as myn, for ye said to me that I shold sprynge on the table.'

'I,' said he, 'I sayd ther lacked salt upon the table.'

'In good feyth I understode,' said she, 'for to spryng.' Thenne was ther laughter ynough and al was taken for a bourd and a 80 mocquerye. Thenne the other two marchauntes said it was no nede to late her sprynge in the basyn, for she had done ynough, and that her husbond had wonne the wager. And she was more preised than the other two that wold not do the commaundement of theyr husbondes.

(*b*) *The ropemaker's wife*

FOR every woman that clenly[1] wylle kepe honoure and worship ought not to abyde alone with a man alone withoute it be with her lord, with her fader or with her sone, and not with ony other. For many evyls and temptacions ben therof come. Of the whiche

[1] clonly

yf I wold I shold reherce you of many of them to whome, as men 5
saie, is evyll happed and also by their nygh parentes. Therfore
it is grete perylle to trust in none, for the devylle is to subtyll to
tempte the flesshe whiche is yong and lusty. Wherfor men ought
to kepe hem self well and take the moost seurest wey. Wherof
I wold ye wyst hou it happed to an evyll wyf whiche was wyf to 10
a roper or cablemaker servynge for shippes and grete vessels upon
the see, and was dwellynge in a good towne.

A man was whiche of his craft was a ropemaker and had a wyf
whiche was not wyse, and the whiche kepte not her feyth and
trouth toward hym but falsed it by the mene of a fals bawde, 15
whiche for a lytel sylver made her to synne and playe with a
pryour that was ryche and a grete lechour. And soo for the
covetyse of a lytell gyft and a lytell jewel, the sayd evylle bawde
maade her to falle in a myschaunt and evylle dede. Wherfor the
sage sayth 'She that taketh, selleth her self'. 20

It happed ones that this pryour was come by nyght and laye
with her. And as he yssued oute of the chambre the fyre beganne
to brenne and gaf lyght. And thenne her husbond sawe hym how
he wente oute, wherof he was affrayed, and sayd he had sene
somme man within the chambre. His wyf made semblaunt as she 25
therof were affrayed, and sayd it was the fende or elles the goblyn
or somme spyryte. But notwithstondyng her sayeng the goodman was therof in grete trystesse and in grete melancolye. The
wyf whiche was malycious and subtyle went anon to another,
her godsep, her neyghbour and bawde, and brought her home 30
with her. The bawde thenne saw how the goodman went aboute
the hows berynge with hym the cordaylle wherwith he made
his cordes. She tooke in her handes a spynroke with blacke wolle
and beganne to spynne. And as he was comynge ageyne toward
her she tooke another with whyte wolle. 35

Thenne sayd to her the goodman whiche was a playne man and
trewe: 'My godsep, me semed that ryght now ye spanne blacke
wolle.'

'Ha, a,' sayd she, 'my godsep, veryly I dyd not soo.'

Thenne wente he fro her ageyne and as he torned ageyne 40
toward her, and that she had taken the other spynrock, he loked

on her and beganne to saye: 'Have, fayre godsep, ye had incontynent a spynrock with whyte wolle?'

'Ha, fayr godsep, what ayleth the now? In good feyth it is not
45 so. I see wel that ye be dasewed and sore dyseased of your syghte and wytte. And in trouthe men wene somtyme to see a thynge that they see not. Ye be thoughtfull and ryght pensyf; certaynly ye have somme thynge that hurteth yow.'

And the goodman that thought she sayd trouthe sayd to her:
50 'By God, godsep, me thought that this last nyght I sawe some body that yssued oute of oure chambre.'

'Ha, a, my good godsep and frend,' sayd the old and fals woman, 'hit was nothynge but the day and the nyght that so bestourned your syght.'

55 Thenne was the goodman wel apayed by the falsenes of the old woman and wend verily she had said trouth.

Afterward it befell another tyme to hym as he supposed to take at his beddes feet a pouche or sack for to have gone with at a market thre myle thens. But he toke with hym the pryours breche
60 and put them under his armes. And thenne whanne he cam to the market and wende to have taken his pouche or lytyll sak, he toke the pryours breche. And as he sawe that, he was sore troubled and wrothe of hit. And the pryour that was voyded and hydde under the bedde wende to have take his breche, but he fonde
65 none sauf the pouche or sak allone. And thenne he knewe well that the goodman had them with hym. Thenne was his wyf at a grete meschyef and wyst not what to do. She wente to her godsep ageyne and told her al the mater and fayt and that she for Goddes sake wold fynde some remedye to it.

70 She sayd to her: 'Ye shal take a payre of breches and I shalle take also another payre, and shalle telle hym that all wymmen were them.' And so they dyde.

Thenne perceyved hym the fals godseb and sawe hym come. She went and welcomed hym and asked hym: 'What chere? Good
75 godsep,' quod she, 'I doubte that ye have fonde some evyll aventure or that ye have lost somme thynge wherof ye be so sadde.'

'Veryly,' sayd the goodman, 'I have lost nothynge, but well I have other thought.'

She dyde so moche that he tolde her alle the matere how that he had founde a payre of breches at hir beddes feet. And whan she herd hym saye thus, she began to lawghe and sayd: 'Ha, my godsep, now I see wel that ye be deceyved and in the weye to be dampned. For in good feythe in alle this towne is none better than is youre wyf ne that more feythfully and clenly kepeth her self toward her husbond than she dothe toward yow. And to putte yow oute of suspecion, trouthe hit is that she and I and many other of thys towne, good wymmen and trewe, have take eche of us a paire of breches and were them for these lechours and putyers that forceth[1] and wylle doo theyr wylles of good wymmen. And to th'ende ye knowe yf I lye or saye trouthe, loke yf I were them or not.'

She tooke up her clothes and shewed hym the breche. And he beheld and sawe that she sayd trouthe and byleved her. And so by suche maner the fals godsep had saved his wyf twyes. But at the laste al evylle wylle be knowen.

The goodman ones sawe his wyf goo into the sayd pryours hows allone, wherof he was ful angry and sorowful; in so moche that incontynently he deffended her and warned her upon payne of lysynge of her eye that never she sholde be so hardy to goo ne converse in the hows of the sayd pryour. But nevertheles she myght never hold her self therfro for the grete temptacion that the fende gaf her. It becam ones that the goodman made semblaunt to goo oute, and played and hyded hym self in a secrete place. And soone after his foole wyf wente into the pryours hows, and her husbond folowed her pas by pas and brought her ageyne and told her that evylle she had kepte his commaundement. Wherfor he bete her.[2] Thenne wente he[3] into the towne and made covenaunt with a cyrurgyen to hele and sette ageyne fast togyder two broken legges. And whanne this covenaunt was made, he cam ageyne to his hows and took a stamper and brake the two legges of his wyf, sayeng to her: 'At the lest shalt thou hold a whyle my commaundement[4] and shalt not go ageynste my deffence there as it pleaseth me not.' And whan he had thus

[1] forced [2] *adds* and brake bothe her legges
[3] she [4] couenaunt

done, he tooke and leyd her in a bed and there she was a grete
115 whyle without departyng.

And atte last the fende mocked her as ye herd tofore, for he made her ever to seke soo many of fowle plesaunces in her folye and in her fowle synne that she[1] myght not chastyse her therof. But whan she was amended of her legges, came the pryour
120 secretely to her. But the goodman herd hym come and doubted hym self, and made semblaunt of slepe and routed. And at the laste soo moche he was herynge them that he herd how he disported hym self with his wyf accomplysshynge and doynge the fowle synne of lecherye. And he tasted aboute and founde well
125 that the dede was trewe. And thenne he wexed so moche angry and wrothe therof that almost he was oute of his memorye and wytte. And drewe oute a grete knyf with a sharp poynte and caste a lytel strawe within the fyre and ranne to them lyghtly and he kylled them bothe at ones. And whanne he had done this
130 dede he called to hym his meyne and his neyghbours and shewed them the faytte or dede. And sente also for the justyse of whiche he was excused and hadde no harme. Ryght moche merveylled the neyghbours how she had tourned her herte to love suche a pryour whiche hadde soo grete a bely and soo thycke and fatte,
135 soo blacke and so fowle of face, and so uncurteys as he was; and her husbond was fayre and good, sage and ryche.

But many wymmen ben lyke and of the nature of the she-wulf, that is the female of the wulf, whiche taketh and cheseth to her love the most fowle and lothly wolf. And soo dothe the folysshe wyf
140 by the temptacion of the fende that ever incessauntly is aboute the synnar, be [i]t man or wyf, to make them to falle in dedely synne. And[2] as the synne is gretter the more he hath myght and puyssaunce over the synnars: and bycause he was a man of relygyon and the woman wedded was the synne gretter. And for
145 certayne by the holy scrypture and wrytynge and as men may al aboute see, yf a woman accomplysshe or doo that synne of lechery with one her kynne and nygh of her blood, she shall be the more temptyd and shal be more brennyng and to it shal have more folyssh appetyte and evyl plesaunce. And therfor it is trewe

[1] he [2] Aind

that so ofte is the pot borne to fetche water that atte laste it 150
breketh in pyeces. For this folysshe wyf whiche hadde a husbond
ten tymes fayrer than the monke was and more curteys and
gracious, and that soo ofte hadde escaped thorugh her fals godseps
delynge, and that upon the defence of her husbond wente ageyne
to the pryours hows, as ye herd tofore, and overmore as the grete 155
anguysshe and dolour that she had suffred of her legges was past,
yet she ne wold chastyse ne kepe her self clene of that fowle synne
of lechery. Thenne is it thyng trewe and approuved that al this is
but temptacion of the devylle whiche holdeth and kepeth the
synnars with brennynge and enflammed hertes to th'ende he may 160
doo them to falle within his grynnes or nettes, as he dyd the sayd
foole woman and to the sayd pryour and made them bothe to
receyve deth vylaynysly.

XV. **Golden Legend** (1483)

St. Ursula and the eleven thousand virgins

IN Brytayn was a cristen kyng named Notus or Maurus, whiche
engendryd a doughter named Ursula. This doughter shone full
of merveylous honeste, wysedome and beaute, and her fame and
renommee was born al aboute. And the Kyng of Englond, whiche
thenne was ryght myghty and subdued many nacions to his 5
empyre, herd the renommee of her and sayde that he shold be
well happy yf this vyrgyne myght be coupled to his sone by
maryage. And the yong man had grete desyre and wyll to have
her. And there was a solempne embassade to the fader of Ursula
and promysed greete promesses and sayd many fayre wordes for 10
to have her, and also made many manaces yf they retourned
vaynly to their lord. And thenne the Kyng of Brytayne beganne
to be moche anguysshous bycause that she that was ennoblysshed
in the faythe of Jhesu Criste shold be wedded to hym that
adoured ydolles, bycause that he wyst well she wold not consente 15
in no manere and also bycause he doubted moche the cruelte of
the Kyng.

And she that was dyvynely inspyred dyd soo moche to her fader that he[1] consented to the maryage by suche a condycion that 20 for to solace her he shold sende to her fader x vyrgyns, and to her self and to them ten other virgyns he shold sende to eche a thousand vyrgyns and sholde gyve to her space of thre yere for to dedycate her vyrgynyte. And the yonge man shold be baptysed and in these thre yere he shold be enformed in the faith 25 sufficiently soo that by wyse counceylle and by vertue of the condycyon made he shold withdrawe fro her his courage. But this yonglyng receyved this condicyon gladly and hasted his fader and was baptysed; and commaunded alle that Ursula had requyred shold be done. And the fader of the vyrgyne ordeyned 30 that his doughter whome he moost lovyd and the other that had nede of comforte of men and servyse, ordeyned in their company good men for to serve them.

Thenne virgynes cam fro alle partyes and men cam for to see this grete companye. And many bisshops cam for to goo with 35 them in theyr pylgremage, emonge whome was Pantulus, Bisshop of Basyle, whiche wente with them to Rome and retorned fro thens with them and receyved martirdome. Saynt Gerasyne, Quene of Scycyle, whiche hadde made of her husbond that was a cruel tyraunt a meke lambe, and was suster of Moryce 40 the bisshop and of Darye moder of Saynt Ursula, to whome the fader of Saynt Ursula had sygnefyed by secrete lettres, she by th'ynspyracion of God put her self in the weye with her foure doughters, Babylla, Juliana, Victorea and Aurea, and her lytel sone Adryan, whiche for love of his susters wente in the same 45 pylgremage, and lefte alle in the hande of her[2] owne sone and cam into Brytayne and saylled over see into Englond. And by the counceyl of thys Quene the virgyns were[3] gadred togydre fro dyverse royammes. And she was ledar of them and at the last she suffryd martirdome with them. And thenne the condycion made, 50 all thynges were made redy.

Thenne the Quene shewed her counceylle to the knyghtes of her companye and made them alle to swere this newe chyvalrye. And thenne beganne they to make dyverse playes and games of

[1] she [2] his [3] wrre

bataylle, as to renne here and there, and fayned many maner of playes. And for alle that they lefte not their purpoos. And somtyme they retourned fro this playe at mydday, and somtyme unnethe at evensonge tyme. And the barons and grete lordes assembled them to see the fayre games and disportes; and alle had joye and playsyre in beholdyng them and also mervaylle. 55

And at the laste whan Ursula hadde convertid all these virgyns unto the faith of Cryst, they wente alle to the see. And in the space of a daye they sailled over the see havynge soo good wynde that they arryved at a porte of Gaule named Tyelle. And fro thens cam to Coloyn where an angel of Our Lord appyeryd to Ursula and tolde her that they shold retorne ageyne the hole nombre to that place and there receyve the crowne of martirdom. And fro thens by the monycyon of the angel they went toward Rome. And whanne they cam to Basyle they lefte there theire shippes and wente to Rome a fote. At the comynge of whome the Pope Ciriacus was moche glad bycause he was borne in Brytayne and hadde many cosyns amonge them. And he with his clerkis receyved them with alle honour. And that same nyght it was shewed to the Pope that he shold receyve with them the crowne of martirdome, whiche thyng he hydde in hym self. And baptisid[1] many of them that were not thenne baptised. 60 65 70 75

And when he sawe tyme covenable, when he had governed the Chirch one yere and enleven wekes and was the xix pope after Peter, he purposed tofore alle the peple and shewed to them his purpoos and resigned his offyce and his dygnyte. But alle men gaynsayd it and specially the cardynallys, whiche supposed that he trespaced levynge the glorye of the papacye and wold goo after this folysshe vyrgyns. But he wold not agree t'abyde, but ordeyned an holy man to occupye in his place, whiche was named Ametus. And bycause he left the syege apostolyque ayenst the wylle of the clergye, the clerkes put oute his name of the cathologue of popes and alle the grace that he had goten in his tyme. This holy companye of wymmen made hym for to leve hit. 80 85

And thenne two felon prynces of the chyvalrye of Rome, Maxymyen and Affrycan, sawe these grete companye of vyrgyns

[1] baptifid

90 and that many men and wymmen assemblyd to them, doubted that crysten relygyon shold moche be encreaced by them. Wherfor they requyred dylygently of their vyage. And thenne sente they messagers to Julyan, theire cosyn, prynce of the lygnage of the Hunes, that he shold brynge his hoost ageynst them, 95 and shold assemble at Coleyne and there byhede them bycause they were crysten.

And the blessyd Cyryake yssued oute of the cyte of Rome with this blessyd company of vyrgyns. And Vyncent, preest-cardynal; and Jaques, that was come fro Brytayne into Antyoche and had 100 holde there seven yere the dignyte of the Bisshop, whiche thenne hadde vysyted the Pope and was gone oute of his cyte and held company with these virgyns whan he herd of their comyng and suffrid martirdome with them; and Mauryce, Bisshop of Levytane the cyte, uncle of Babylle and Julyan; and Folarius, Bisshop 105 of Lucence, with Supplyce, Bisshop of Ravenne, whiche thenne were come to Rome, put them in the companye of these virgyns.

Ethereus, the husbond of Ursula, abydyng in Britayne was warned of Our Lord by a vysyon of an angel that he shold exhorte his moder to be crysten, for his fader deyde the fyrste 110 yere that he was crystned. And Ethereus his sone succeded after hym in his regne. And thenne whan these holy vyrgyns retorned fro Rome with the bisshops, Ethereus was warned of Oure Lord that he shold anone aryse and goo to mete his wyf at Coleyne and there receyve with her the crowne of martirdome. The 115 whiche anone obeyed to admonestements dyvyne: and dyd do baptyse his moder and cam with her and his lytel suster Florence, thenne also baptysed, and with the Bisshop Clement, metynge the holy virgyns and accompanyed them unto martirdome. And Marculus, Bisshop of Grece, and his nece Constaunce, doughter 120 of Dorothe Kynge of Constantynople, which was maryed to the sone of a kynge but he deyde tofore the weddyng and she avowed to Our Lord her vyrgynyte, they were also warned by a vysyon and cam to Rome and joyned them to these vyrgyns unto the martirdome.

125 And thenne alle these vyrgyns cam with the bisshops to Coleyne and fonde that it was besyeged with the Hunes. And whan

the Hunes sawe them, they beganne to renne upon them with a grete crye and araged lyke wolves on shepe and slewe alle this grete multitude. And whanne they were al byheded they cam to the blessyd Ursule. And the Prynce of them seyng her beaute soo 130 merveylous was abasshed and began to comforte her upon the dethe of the vyrgyns and promysed to her to take her to his wyf. And whan she hadde refused hym and despysed hym at all, he shote at her an arow and perced her thorugh the body, and so accomplysshed her martirdome. And one of the vyrgyns whiche 135 was named Cordula was sore aferd and hydde her self alle that nyght in a ship. But on the morn she suffrid deth by her free wylle and toke the crowne of martirdome. And bycause her feest was not holde with the other vyrgynes she appierid longe after to a recluse and commaunded hym that the next daye folowynge the 140 feste of the virgyns her feest shold be remembryd. They suffrid dethe the yere of Our Lord ccxxxviij. But somme holde oppynyon that the reason of the tyme sheweth that they suffred not dethe in that tyme, for Cecylle ne Constantynople were thenne no royammes. But it is supposed that they suffryd deth longe 145 tyme after whanne Constaunt was Emperour, and that the Hunes and Gothes enforced them ageynste crysten men in the tyme of th'Emperour Marcyen that regned in the yere of Oure Lord four c lix.

Hit is to be remembryd that amonge these enleven thousand 150 vyrgyns were many men, for the Pope Cyryaque and other bisshops and Ethereus Kynge with other lordes and knyghtes hadde moche peple to serve them. And as I have ben enformed in Coleyn that there were men besyde wymmen that thylke tyme suffryd martirdome fyften thousand. So the nombre of this hooly 155 multitude as of the hooly vyrgyns and men were xxvj^{m}, to whom late us praye to Our Lord that he have mercy on us.

Ther was an Abbot that impetred of th'Abbesse of the place where these holy vyrgyns reste in Coleyn a body of one of these virgyns, and promysed that he wold sette it in his chirche in a 160 fayre shryne of sylver. But whan he hadde kepte it a yere upon the aulter in a cheste of tree and in a nyght as th'Abbot songe matyns, the sayd vyrgyne descended fro the aulter bodyly and

enclyned honourably tofore the aulter and wente thorugh the
165 choer seeynge alle the monkes, whiche were therof sore abasshed. And thenne th'Abbot ranne and fonde it al voide and nothynge therin. Thenne th'Abbotte wente to Coleyne and told to th'Abbesse alle the thynge by ordre. Thenne wente they to the place where they had taken the body and fonde the same there ageyne.
170 And thenne th'Abbot requyred pardon and prayd th'Abbesse that he myght have ageyne the same body or another, promysyng ryght certaynly to make hastely a precious shryne. But he couthe none have in no manere.

Ther was a relygyous monke whiche had grete devocion to
175 these hooly vyrgyns. And it happed that he was on a day seke and sawe a ryght fayre and noble vyrgyne appiere to hym and demaunded hym yf he knewe her. And he was amerveyled of this vysyon and sayde he knewe her not. And she sayd: 'I am one of the virgyns to whome thow hast suche grete devocion. And therof
180 thow shalt have a reward. Yf thou saye enleven thowsand Pater Nosters for the love and honour of us, we shalle come unto thyne ayde and comforte at the houre of thy dethe.' And thenne she vanysshed awey and he accomplysshed her request as soone as he myght. And anone after he dyde doo calle his Abbot and dyd
185 hym to be eneled or enoynted. And as they enoynted hym he cryed sodenly: 'Make ye place to the holy vyrgyns and go out of the waye that they may come to me.' And whan th'Abbot demaunded hym what it was and what he mente, he tolde to hym by ordre the promesse of the vyrgyne. Thenne alle they with-
190 drewe them a lytel after; and sone cam ageyne and fonde hym departed oute of this world unto Our Lord.

Thenne late us devoutely gyve lawde and praysynge unto the blessyd Trynyte and praye hym that by the merytes of this grete multitude of martirs he wolle foryeve and pardone us of oure
195 synnes that after this lyf we may come unto this holy companye in heven. Amen.

XVI. **Order of Chivalry** (1484)

Epilogue

HERE endeth the book of th'*Ordre of Chyvalry*, whiche book is translated oute of Frensshe into Englysshe at a requeste of a gentyl and noble esquyer by me, William Caxton, dwellynge in Westmynstre besyde London in the most best wyse that God hath suffred me and accordynge to the copye that the sayd squyer 5 delyverd to me. Whiche book is not requysyte to every comyn man to have, but to noble gentylmen that by their vertu entende to come and entre into the noble ordre of chyvalry, the whiche in these late dayes hath [not] ben used accordyng to this booke heretofore wreton, but forgeten, and th'excersytees of chyvalry 10 not used, honoured ne excercysed as hit hath ben in auncyent tyme. At whiche tyme the noble actes of the knyghtes of Englond that used chyvalry were renomed thurgh the unyversal world. As for to speke tofore th'yncarnacion of Jhesu Cryste, where were there ever ony lyke to Brenius and Belynus that from the grete 15 Brytayne, now called Englond, unto Rome and ferre beyonde conquered many royammes and londes, whos noble actes remayne in th'old hystoryes of the Romayns? And syth the incarnacion of Oure Lord byhold that noble Kyng of Brytayne, Kyng Arthur, with al the noble knyghtes of the round table, whos 20 noble actes and noble chyvalry of his knyghtes occupye soo many large volumes, that is a world or as thyng incredyble to byleve. O ye knyghtes of Englond, where is the custome and usage of noble chyvalry that was used in tho dayes? What do ye now but go to the baynes and playe atte dyse? And some not wel advysed 25 use not honest and good rule ageyn alle ordre of knyghthode. Leve this. Leve it and rede the noble volumes of Saynt Graal, of Lancelot, of Galaad, of Trystram, of Perse Forest, of Percyval, of Gawayn and many mo. Ther shalle ye see manhode, curtosye and gentylnesse. And loke in latter dayes of the noble actes 30 syth the conquest, as in Kyng Rychard dayes Cuer du Lyon, Edward the fyrste and the thyrd and his noble sones, Syre Robert Knolles, Syr Johan Hawkwode, Syr Johan Chaundos

and Syre Gaultier Mauny.[1] Rede Froissart. And also behold
35 that vyctoryous and noble Kynge Harry the fyfthe and the
capytayns under hym, his noble bretheren, th'Erle of Salysbury
Montagu and many other whoos names shyne gloryously by
their vertuous noblesse and actes that they did in th'onour of
th'ordre of chyvalry.

40 Allas! what doo ye but slepe and take ease and ar al disordred
fro chyvalry? I wold demaunde a question yf I shold not displease.
How many knyghtes ben ther now in Englond that have th'use
and th'excercyse of a knyghte, that is to wete that he knoweth his
hors and his hors hym, that is to saye he beynge redy at a poynt
45 to have al thyng that longeth to a knyght, an hors that is accordyng and broken after his hand, his armures and harnoys mete and
syttyng and so forth et cetera? I suppose and a due serche shold
be made ther shold be many founden that lacke, the more pyte
is. I wold it pleasyd oure soverayne lord that twyes or thryes in a
50 yere or at the lest ones he wold do crye justes of pees to th'ende
that every knyght shold have hors and harneys and also the use
and craft of a knyght, and also to tornoye one ageynste one or ij
ageynst ij and the best to have a prys, a dyamond or jewel, suche
as shold please the Prynce. This shold cause gentylmen to resorte
55 to th'auncyent custommes of chyvalry to grete fame and renommee, and also to be alwey redy to serve theyr prynce whan he
shalle calle them or have nede. Thenne late every man that
is come of noble blood and entendeth to come to the noble
ordre of chyvalry rede this lytyl book and doo therafter in
60 kepyng the lore and commaundements therin comprysed. And
thenne I doubte not he shall atteyne to th'ordre of chyvalry
et cetera.

And thus thys lytyl book I presente to my redoubted, naturel
and most dradde soverayne lord, Kyng Rychard, Kyng of
65 Englond and of Fraunce, to th'ende that he commaunde this book
to be had and redde unto other yong lordes, knyghtes and gentylmen within this royame that the noble ordre of chyvalrye be
herafter better used and honoured than hit hath ben in late dayes
passed. And herin he shalle do a noble and vertuouse dede. And

[1] Manuy

I shalle praye almyghty God for his long lyf and prosperous 70
welfare and that he may have victory of al his enemyes and after
this short and transitory lyf to have everlastyng lyf in heven where
as is joye and blysse world without ende. Amen.

871081 X I

NOTES

[In the Notes, *OED* refers to *The Oxford English Dictionary* edited by J. A. H. Murray *et al.* (1930); Godefroy to *Dictionnaire de l'ancienne langue française* (1881–1902); and EETS to the Early English Text Society.]

I (*a*)

S. K. Workman, in 'Versions by Skelton, Caxton, and Berners of a Prologue by Diodorus Siculus', *Modern Language Notes*, lvi (1941), 252–8, has shown that the first part of Caxton's prologue is based on the prologue to the *Historical Library* by Diodorus the Sicilian. The first five books of the Greek text were translated into Latin by Poggio Bracciolini, but Caxton's version is probably based on a French adaptation of Poggio which is no longer extant. Poggio's Latin was translated into English by John Skelton about 1485, edited in F. M. Salter and H. L. R. Edwards, *The Bibliotheca Historica of Diodorus Siculus translated by John Skelton* (EETS, 1956–7); and his version of the prologue by Lord Berners in his translation of Froissart's *Chronicles*, edited in W. P. Ker, *The Chronicle of Froissart translated out of French by Sir John Bourchier, Lord Berners* (London, 1901), i. 3–7. Berners, like Caxton, added his own remarks at the end of Diodorus' generalizations to make the prologue more suitable for his own translation.

Workman notes that Caxton, in his treatment of the text, stands between Berners and Skelton: he is less expansive and aureate than Skelton, but more ornate than Berners. He goes on to claim that 'Structurally the prose [of Caxton's translation] is firmer, more accurate, and more patterned than that in any of Caxton's original writing. Within this very prologue the difference may be observed, Caxton's typical looseness beginning at the point where he gave over his source and began on his own' (p. 256).

6. Emendation seems best here, for we would expect a verb in the relative clause; cf. the corresponding sentence in Berners: 'For when we (beynge unexpert of chaunces) se, beholde, and rede the auncyent actes, gestes, and dedes, howe and with what labours, daungers, and paryls they were gested and done, they right greatly admonest, ensigne, and teche us howe we maye lede forthe our lyves.'

43. *pryvate men*: cf. Skelton's 'persones ful symple of havoir, and comen of baas & lowe progenye'.

55. On the use of *many of* see *OED*, *Many*, A. *adj*. 3. As this usage is rare, Caxton probably took it over literally from the French.

57. *lyteral monumentis*: cf. 'litterarum monumentis' (Poggio), 'motyf of litterature' (Skelton).

76. Their time in this world soon passes out of human remembrance, because it is so uneventful. Consequently, neither their life nor their death is remembered. Cf. Skelton's 'whos maner of lyuynge here & fynall departynge out of this lyf present is rasyd with oblyuyon oute of remembraunce, so as of their dedely conuersacion ensieweth after their deth noo famous memorial'.

89. *distributed in dyverse chaunges*: scattered and hence destroyed through the changes wrought by time. Cf. Berners's 'in processe of tyme by varyable chaunces are confused and lost'.

93. In Diodorus the relevance of this paragraph is more explicit, for history is said to assist eloquence and hence to be that much more valuable.

99. It is difficult to make sense of this sentence without emendation. That proposed here is suggested by the occurrence of (*it*) *may be* elsewhere in the prologue (e.g. ll. 63, 65). The sense is better if the *it* is taken to refer to history. Cf. Skelton's 'Thenne, syth vertue historyall is onely suche a maistresse by whome men emonge theym-self alle other excelle, thenne it semeth it is thynge as precyous and of so grete valewe as euer was the florysshynge courage & polisshed eloquence of lusty vtteraunce'. For the omission of the pronoun subject (*it*) *causeth* see P. de Reul, *The Language of Caxton's Reynard the Fox* (London and Ghent, 1901), pp. 30–2.

102. Cf. Skelton's 'delyten the mynde of man with wanton pleasure rather than it prouffyteth'. An emendation in Caxton's text seems necessary to complete the antithesis which was clearly intended: 'more to pleasure than to profit'.

104–5. By dressing up fiction in verisimilitude they encourage lies and deceit.

116. Caxton's version of the *Golden Legend* was published in 1483; an extract from it is given as No. XV below.

123. Edward's reign began on 4 Mar. 1461. As the new year was then reckoned from 25 Mar., Edward's reign began in 1460, according to the old reckoning.

124. *As* may be understood as a loose connective with what has gone before; translate 'in such wise as'. For the omission of the subject pronoun see note to l. 99.

126. Ranulph Higden entered St. Werburgh's monastery, Chester, in 1299. His original version of the *Polychronicon* covered the period extending from the Creation to about 1342, though various continuations were made by others. He died in 1364. The versions of Higden and Trevisa are edited by C. Babington and J. R. Lumby, *Polychronicon Ranulphi Higden Monachi Cestrensis* (London, 1865–86). See also J. Taylor, *The Universal Chronicle of Ranulph Higden* (Oxford, 1966).

128. After being expelled from Oxford in 1379, John de Trevisa (1326–1412) became vicar of Berkeley in Gloucestershire. He translated Higden's *Polychronicon* in 1387 and added a short continuation which ends with an account of the Treaty of Brétigny (1360). Trevisa translated the *De Proprietatibus Rerum* of Bartholomaeus Anglicus in 1389, which was later printed by Wynkyn de Worde. His translation of the Bible, if he made one, has not survived. See D. C. Fowler, 'John Trevisa and the English Bible', *Modern Philology*, lviii (1960–1), 81–98, and his 'New Light on John Trevisa', *Traditio*, xviii (1962), 289–317.

132. Caxton made the work more attractive by an attempt at modernizing the language: see Babington and Lumby, op. cit. i, pp. lxiv–lxvi.

133. A selection from Caxton's continuation, usually known as the *Liber Ultimus*, is reproduced as No. II below.

135. In his epilogue to Book VII Caxton repeats the date 1357 for the end of Trevisa's work, though it really finished in 1360.

I (*b*)

1 ff. The *hystoryes* would probably comprise the *Polychronicon* (1482) and the *Golden Legend* (1483), and the *bookes of ensaumples* are probably the *Book of the Knight of the Tower* (1484) and *Æsop's Fables* (1484).

4. Caxton suggests that he had many inquiries about a book on King Arthur, though it would seem that he printed Malory for one unidentified person in particular (cf. ll. 45, 89).

6. Note the use of both a past participle *made* and an infinitive *enprynte* after *do*. For other examples of this usage in Caxton see L. Kellner, *Caxton's Blanchardyn and Eglantine, c. 1489* (EETS, 1890), pp. lxiii–lxiv.

11. For the Nine Worthies see M. Y. Offord, *The Parlement of the Thre Ages* (EETS, 1959), pp. xl–xlii.

14–16. The first book Caxton printed was the *History of Troy*; see No. X below.

28. Caxton printed his version of *Charles the Great* in this same year, though he does not refer to it; see No. IV below.

30. *Godfrey of Bouillon* or *The Siege and Conquest of Jerusalem* was printed in 1481; see No. III below.

39–40. For the growth and development of the Arthurian legend see particularly *Arthurian Literature in the Middle Ages. A Collaborative History*, edited by R. S. Loomis (Oxford, 1959).

49. The *ye may see* may be understood to apply to the second half of the sentence as well.

49–50. Avalon was often identified with Glastonbury, where in the late twelfth century some large bones were excavated and taken to be Arthur's.

50. *Polycronycon*. See note to No. I (*a*), l. 126. Higden was in fact sceptical about Arthur, though both passages mention the finding of the bones and their reinterment.

53–4. Boccaccio's *De Casibus Virorum Illustrium* (1355–74) was usually known in English as 'The Fall of Princes'.

55. Geoffrey of Monmouth's *Historia Regum Britanniae* was written shortly after 1135. In medieval legend Brutus was the grandson of Æneas and the founder of Britain.

61–2. Gawain, the son of Arthur's half-sister Morgause, figures in many Arthurian romances; Cradock, or Carados, plays a minor role in several Arthurian stories, but he is the central figure in the late ballad *The Boy and the Mantle*.

62. This round table may still be seen at Winchester affixed to the wall of the Great Hall, now the Assize Court.

71. Camelot is the legendary seat of Arthur's court, which has been variously identified. Here Caxton equates it with Caerleon (Monmouthshire) where, according to Geoffrey of Monmouth, Arthur was crowned. Caerleon contains Roman remains and a ruined early medieval castle.

81. Caxton spent many years in the Low Countries.

89. For Sir Thomas Malory see W. Matthews, *The Ill-framed Knight* (Berkeley and Los Angeles, 1966), and E. Vinaver, *The Works of Sir Thomas Malory*, 2nd edn. (Oxford, 1967), i, pp. xii–xxviii.

II

The *Liber Ultimus* is the continuation Caxton made to Trevisa's translation of Higden's *Polychronicon*. It is based largely on his edition of the *Chronicles of England* (1480, 2nd edn. 1482), though for the reign of Richard II Caxton had at least two sources. The continuation is edited in C. Babington and J. R. Lumby, *Polychronicon Ranulphi Higden Monachi Cestrensis* (London, 1865–86), viii. 522–87, and W. Blades, *The Life and Typography of William Caxton* (London and Strasbourg, 1861–3), i. 197–265. On this period in general see R. Bird, *The Turbulent London of Richard II* (London, 1949).

1. Richard II, second son of the Black Prince and Joan of Kent, was born at Bordeaux on 6 Jan. 1367. He succeeded Edward III on 22 June 1377.

10. The poll-tax by which everyone was to pay three groats in tax was one of the immediate causes of the Peasants' Revolt of 1381. See C. Oman, *The Great Revolt of 1381* (Oxford, 1906; reissued 1969).

14. *Hurlyng* is here used in the sense 'strife, disturbance'; hence *hurlyng tyme* is a time of tumult. This descriptive phrase was applied by later medieval chroniclers particularly to the Peasants' Revolt.

16. The Thursday after Trinity Sunday: in 1381, Thursday 13 June.

17–18. The King's Bench and the Marshalsea were prisons in Southwark.

18–19. The anger of the insurgents was particularly directed at the Flemings, who were thought to deprive the English of their work; cf. Chaucer, *The Nun's Priest's Tale*, ll. 574–6.

21–2. Simon Sudbury, Archbishop of Canterbury, was Chancellor of England and was popularly held responsible for the poll-tax. Sir Robert Hales, the Prior of St. John's, was in charge of the Treasury.

26. The Savoy was the London palace of John of Gaunt, Duke of Lancaster, who was very unpopular at this time, particularly in London. Gaunt himself was in Scotland during the revolt.

28. The rebels seized all those who had fled into sanctuary for safety and killed some of them, notably Roger Legett, who was torn from the high

altar of St. Martin's-le-Grand, and John Imworth, who was seized at the shrine of Edward the Confessor in Westminster Abbey.

29–30. Cf. 'and made hem gone out of the seyntuarye al that were within for ony maner of grith' (*Chronicles of England*, 1482); *ony maner grythe*: 'any kind of asylum'.

30–1. The buildings belonging to the lawyers, the Temple and the Inns of Court, were burned because the lawyers were held to be partly responsible for the enslavement of poor people since they drew up the writs.

33. Newgate was a London prison situated near the Old Bailey.

38. Although several fifteenth-century chronicles record this story of Jack Straw, it was in fact Wat Tyler who was killed by Walworth at Smithfield.

50. The Londoners had alienated Richard by their refusal to provide him with £1,000 and by an attack on a Lombard banker who was willing to provide the money.

79. Anne of Bohemia was Richard's first wife; she died in June 1394.

80. *Gravesende*. This clause is not found in the *Chronicles of England* which were published by Caxton in 1480 and 1482 and which were his main source for the *Liber Ultimus*. There was no bishop of London named Gravesend during Richard II's reign, but a Richard Gravesend, who died in 1303, and a Stephen Gravesend his nephew, who died in 1338, had both been bishops of London in their day. Probably the Gravesend here mentioned is meant to be one of these two. It is likely that Caxton introduced this erroneous sentence either from memory or from one of his subsidiary sources.

82. Edward the Confessor was the founder of Westminster Abbey, which is dedicated to him. Richard is said to have been particularly attached to his shrine.

88. London had to pay heavily to regain its privileges; the gifts to Richard on this occasion are said to have included a camel.

94. Richard married Isabel, then only eight years old, on 12 Mar. 1396. The marriage was part of Richard's policy of appeasement towards France.

104. There was a royal palace at Kennington.

116. Thomas of Woodstock (1355–97), Duke of Gloucester since 1385, was the youngest son of Edward III. He was the leader of the Lords Appellant against Richard.

125. Brest had in fact been pledged to the English in 1378; the town was returned to the French in April 1397, upon payment of the pledges.

131. *our cosyn* . . .: the Duke of Brittany.

138. *Marchal.* The Earl Marshal was Thomas Mowbray, Earl of Nottingham. He was created Duke of Norfolk later in 1397 in reward for his services. Because he was Captain of Calais he was held by some to have been responsible for Gloucester's murder.

158. Thomas Arundel had been consecrated Archbishop of Canterbury in 1396.

167. Henry Bolingbroke, Earl of Derby, was John of Gaunt's son, and was created Duke of Hereford by Richard II in 1397. The reasons behind his quarrel with Norfolk are not clear.

180 ff. In the latter part of his reign Richard, who was impecunious, tried to raise money by various means. The men mentioned here were popularly held responsible for the repressive measures.

183. Edmund of Langley (1342–1402) was the fourth son of Edward III.

186. *Powlus*: St. Paul's.

197. Richard had in fact sequestered the revenues and property belonging to the duchy of Lancaster.

207–9. The lords and people are those in Richard's army. Caxton uses two finite verbs where we would use a present participle and a finite verb: 'Understanding that . . . they began to murmur'. For the omission of the subject pronoun *they* see note to No. I (*a*), l. 99.

228. Nicholas Slake, Dean of the King's Chapel, had been arrested by the Appellants in 1387.

240. Henry IV was crowned on 13 Oct. 1399.

244. Roger Walden had been made archbishop upon Arundel's exile.

249. Edward of Langley, Earl of Rutland, was the son of the Duke of York (see note to 183). He was created Duke of Albemarle in 1397, but reverted to Earl of Rutland in 1399. Conclusive evidence for his betrayal is lacking.

313. *Langley*: King's Langley, Hertfordshire, where there was a Dominican priory.

317. Sir John Holland, Earl of Huntingdon and for a time Duke of Exeter, was Richard's half-brother.

III

Historia Rerum in Partibus Transmarinis Gestarum, an account of the First Crusade and the French establishments in the Holy Land, was written by William, Archbishop of Tyre (1175–84). Its principal hero was Godfrey of Bouillon, one of the Nine Worthies (see No. I (*b*), l. 30). A modern English translation of William's Latin text is available in E. A. Babcock and A. C. Krey, *A History of Deeds done beyond the Sea* (New York, 1943). A French translation of the Latin was made in the early thirteenth century and Caxton's version was translated from the French. The French text has been edited by P. Paris, *Guillaume de Tyr et ses continuateurs* (Paris, 1879). This edition has been used as a basis for comparison with Caxton's text here, although it is different in several details from the manuscript that Caxton used. Caxton's version has been edited by M. N. Colvin, *Godeffroy of Boloyne or The Siege and Conqueste of Jerusalem* (EETS, 1893). Miss Colvin collated Caxton's text with the French version in Bibliothèque nationale MS. 68. It is not certain that this is the manuscript that Caxton used, for a full-scale collation of the French manuscripts, which are numerous, has never been carried out.

Pope Urban launched the First Crusade at the Council of Clermont (1095). His plea was echoed by the preachers, notably Peter the Hermit, and the response, particularly among the lower classes, was considerable. The crusaders were to assemble at Constantinople, and the majority of the poorer people and some of the lesser nobility decided to march there under Peter's leadership. The march took place in 1096.

3. Walter Sans-Avoir left Peter at Cologne on Easter Tuesday, 1096. Some of the French manuscripts read *Gautiers sans savoir* instead of *Gautiers sans avoir*, and Caxton used one of these.

10–11. King Coloman of Hungary (1095–1116).

16. *good cheep*: 'à bon marché'; i.e. at a reasonable price.

18. *Marce*. The French has *Maroé*. It is not possible to decide whether Caxton's French original, as yet unidentified, had *Marce*, whether Caxton misread the word, or whether this is a typographical error (cf. ll. 93, 155). The Maroe (the Latin has *Maros*) must be the modern river Morawa, though the geographical description fits the river Save better. Upon crossing the river the pilgrims entered the Byzantine empire.

20. *Bongrye*: consistently spelled with an *n*, though one would have expected Bougrye, as in the French, for Bulgaria.

22. *Mallevylle*: Semlin (Zemun).

32. *Bellegrave*: Belgrade.

52. *Stralyce*: probably Sophia.

52–3. *Danemarche the moyen*: cf. 'Danemarch la meine' (French), 'Stralicia Daciae mediterraneae metropolis' (Latin). This was a diocese of the Eastern Church.

61. *th'Emperour*: Alexius I Comnenus, Byzantine emperor (1081–1118).

71. *xl^m*: forty thousand.

86–7. *and ran to armes and began every man to do wel*: cf. 'si courent aus armes et s'entrecomencent à semondre et à amonester de bien faire'.

93. *Incita*: cf. *Nicita* (French), *Niceta* (Latin), and see note to l. 18.

103. Peter is the subject of *doubted*.

105. The banks of the river Save are meant; cf. 'et en la rive devers lui et en l'autre'.

112. *Nyze*: Nish in Serbia (Yugoslavia), still an important transport centre.

113–14. Cf. 'de granz tours et de forz murs'.

140. *Duchemen*: 'Germans'. There were many Germans among Peter's followers, for he had stopped to preach at Cologne. The French text is more severe in its comments on the Germans.

150. The whole army was held responsible for what these few had done.

155. *thre*: the French has *tyois* 'German'; either Caxton misread this as *trois* or the corruption was contained in the manuscript he was using.

159–60. *mal[ad]es, servauntes*: cf. 'malades, vieilles genz'. Caxton has not followed the French closely here, yet it seems preferable to emend *males* to *malades*, even though these words are confused in some Old French manuscripts.

173. *disconvenyents*: 'causes for sorrow and grief'; a nonce word taken over from the French. This sentence echoes that at l. 171.

186. The French text contains a couple of lines, which are not found in Caxton, to the effect that when peace was almost settled a great noise was heard.

188–9. Cf. 'Pierres senti que ceste chose tourneroit à mal'.

190. In the French these great men are sent to pacify those in Peter's company who were causing so much disturbance.

217. i.e. with such armour and arms as they had there; they did not stop to make proper preparations for a battle.

235. *territorie*. The French has *tertre* 'a small hill', the Latin *in collem*. Translate as 'hill'.

237. The French has thirty thousand.

239. *they lefte not* . . .: cf. 'ne lessierent mie por ce, que il ne se méissent à la voie que il avoient emprise'.

241. *poynt*: the meeting took place in Sophia.

255. *with you*: cf. 'avant vous'.

IV

Works about Charlemagne were popular throughout the Middle Ages, as such poems as the *Chanson de Roland* reveal. In the fourteenth century a poetic romance, usually known as *Fierabras*, was composed in France about Charlemagne's exploits. The poem became well known, and soon after the introduction of the printing-press into France, several prose versions of the poem were printed. One of these was 'imprime a genesue Par maistre Loys Garbin bourgois de la dicte cite. Lan mil cccc.lxxxiij. et Le .xiij. iour de moys de Mars'. It was this text that Caxton used for his translation. As with *Reynard the Fox*, the continental version reached Caxton very quickly after it was printed, for in both cases Caxton's translation appeared only two years after the continental text was issued. Caxton's text is edited by S. J. H. Herrtage, *The Lyf of the Noble and Crysten Prynce, Charles the Grete* (EETS, 1880–1).

6. *at this stroke*: a literal translation of the French which reads *a cestuy cop*, with the sense here 'immediately'; see Godefroy, s.v. *Cop*.

15. *bowed*: 'bent'. The sense of *bowed and entred* seems to be that the lances bent as they pierced the shields. The sentence is translated almost literally from the French 'sont par force ploiez et entrez dedens dont le feu partit'.

25. Understand 'he' as the subject of *made to flee*, i.e. 'to fly'.

36–7. *I have wel herde the spoken*: 'I have heard what you said', cf. 'je t'ay bien oy parler'. Caxton may have misread *parler* as *parlé*.

48–9. *afterward*: cf. 'par derriere'.

63. *for the the best*: 'the best thing for you (to do)'.

71. *dysmesured*: Caxton has taken over the French *desmesuré* 'proudly' and given it an English form: cf. *dysmesurably*, l. 304.

80. A prayer uttered by Charles while watching the fight is omitted.

90. Oliver here says a prayer similar in content to that spoken by Charles at ll. 200–24.

116. *he*: 'they' would be more suitable; cf. 'Qu'ilz luy voulsissent garantir l'ame'. Caxton frequently confuses the pronouns found in his source.

122. *he coude do* is best understood to refer to Fierabras. 'No matter what Fierabras might do, Oliver would not take the potion even though he should die (as a result of that refusal).' This clause is not in the French.

137–8. *made a lytel course*: 'galloped off a short distance'.

158. *inpytuously*: 'vigorously'; the French has *impetueusement.*

159. The subject of *fyl* is Oliver's horse.

162–3. *above hys propre custome*: 'contrary to his usual practice'; cf. 'oultre sa propre acoustumance'.

171. *a foure paas nyghe*: 'four paces in front of Fierabras'.

172. *the foule*: *the* is the accusative singular of the 2nd personal pronoun, and *foule* is an adverb. The sense is 'you have behaved shamefully'.

176. Caxton has added the *no*, which is not in the French. *(H)eritage* here means 'what falls to one's portion through conquest'.

183. *thys hors present.* One must understand a part of the verb 'to be'; cf. 'il fust present'.

207. *whyche was of knowyng good and evyl*: cf. 'celluy de vie'.

214. For the blindness of Longinus and its healing see R. J. Peebles, *The Legend of Longinus* (Bryn Mawr, 1911).

216. *of:* 'some of'.

225–6. *in hys secrete oratorye*: cf. 'en son secret'.

232. *medytacyon.* This is also the reading in the French which must mean 'thought, plan'. It is possible, though, that the French reading is a mistake for *mediacion.*

234–5. The French is clearer: 'Fierabras per grant fureur voult fraper Olivier.'

290–1. *ne for to deye therfore*: 'not even if I die on account of that'; cf. l. 122. See also *OED*, *For, prep.* VII. 23. c.

361–3. The *that anone thou . . .* clause may also be understood to be dependent upon *Now is the houre come.*

V

The first branch of the French *Roman de Renart* served as the basis for the Dutch poem *Van den Vos Reynaerde*. A prose adaptation of an expanded version of this poem was printed by Gerard Leeu at Gouda in 1479. Caxton translated Leeu's text. It is the only known translation that he made from Dutch, and there are many Dutch words and expressions in the text. On Caxton's translation see N. F. Blake, 'William Caxton's *Reynard the Fox* and his Dutch Original', *Bulletin of the John Rylands Library*, xlvi (1963–4), 298–325, and *Reynard the Fox* (EETS, 1970).

5. *the booke*: a Bible or a collection of saints' lives.

11. Dame Rukenawe, Reynard's aunt, had advised him how to conduct himself in the duel. It was she who prompted him to cut off his hair and oil his body, and to urinate into his tail.

30. *strode wyder*: 'took longer steps'; the phrase is translated literally from the Dutch.

58. *buff ne baff*: an alliterative expression found in both English and Dutch (*boe noch bau*), meaning 'not a single word'.

76. *ful of stufs*: the Dutch has *vol stofs*. Caxton not only transliterated the Dutch word exactly, which he normally translated 'dust', but he also included an *of* for the genitive case expressed by the *-s* in Dutch.

85–6. This refers to a previous exploit in which Reynard had got Noble the lion to strip Isegrim of the skin round his paws to serve as gloves for him on his intended pilgrimage.

138. *wynnyng for your cloistre*. Caxton probably did not understand the Dutch *cloester winninghe*, which means gaining a share in the good deeds of the monks in order to mitigate one's own sins, *opera supererogatoria*.

163. *but I thought it never*: 'such a thought never entered my head'.

215. This refers to another trick which Reynard had perpetrated on the wolf's wife. She got stuck in the ice when trying to catch fish with her tail, and Reynard had taken advantage of her plight to rape her. It was one of the main causes of the present duel.

235. *take it up into his handes*: 'decide the matter himself'.

238. The *lossem* is the same animal as the *losse* (l. 4). Caxton has taken over this form, which cannot adequately be explained, from the Dutch. Translate 'lynx'.

VI

Caxton's reasons for printing Sir Thomas Malory's *Le Morte d'Arthur* are given in his prologue (see No. I (*b*)). Caxton found it necessary to make extensive alterations to Book V, from which this passage is taken, because Malory had used the Middle English alliterative poem, *Morte Arthure*, as his source for it: it consequently contained many old alliterative words and phrases. Caxton's text formed the basis of all modern editions till the finding of the unique Winchester manuscript in 1934, and it still remains valuable as that manuscript is not complete. Caxton's Book V, the book he adapted most, is printed in full with Malory's text in E. Vinaver, *The Works of Sir Thomas Malory*, 2nd edn. (Oxford, 1967).

3. *utas of Hyllary*: the octave of (or the eighth day following) the feast of St. Hilary, i.e. 20 Jan.

8–9. If, as has been suggested by Vinaver, Malory intended Arthur's expedition to the Continent to mirror Henry V's campaigns, then Sir Baudwin and Sir Constantine would represent the Duke of Bedford and Cardinal Beaufort respectively. The accession of Constantine after Arthur's death is mentioned at the end of *Le Morte d'Arthur*.

8–9. *for to counceille to the best*: 'to advise what was best'. This phrase has been taken from a different context in Malory to be applied by Caxton to Sir Baudwin.

12–14. This sentence does not occur in the alliterative *Morte Arthure*, and the reason for its inclusion by Malory remains doubtful. The story of Tristram and Isolde is not given till Book VIII.

35. In Malory the animal is a bear, which Caxton probably altered to a boar because of the tusks, but he forgot to alter the 'pawes as bygge as a post'.

35–6. Malory's *to-rongeled with lugerande lokys* 'shaggy with locks of hair hanging down' may not have been understood by Caxton, whose own reading is not without its difficulties. His *he was rugged, lokynge roughly* may perhaps be interpreted 'it was all hairy and rough looking'.

45. *to powdre*: 'to dust'; in Malory the dragon destroys the boar by fire.

57–8. Caxton has added *beynge horryble and abhomynable whoos pere ye sawe never in your dayes*. Because he simply joined it on to the end of the existing sentence, it seems to refer to *thy self* (Arthur), but of course it refers to the giant.

59. *comeforth*: in Caxton's printed text this appears as *come forth*, which may have been the reading Caxton intended, for the spelling of *comfort* with an internal *e* is rare. But Malory has *comforte* and the *Morte Arthure comforth*.

61. Caxton has added *in Flaundres*, possibly because at an earlier point Lucius was said to have got his troops ready there. But *Barflete* is Barfleur in Normandy. The mistake is unexpected since Caxton had lived for many years in Flanders.

65–6. *Constantyn*: the Cotentin; *besyde Bretayn*, i.e. Brittany, was added by Caxton possibly because the Duchess of Brittany was kidnapped by the giant.

67–8. *had ben susteyned . . . with*: 'had fed on'.

72. *montayne*: St. Michael's Mount, a rocky island accessible at low tide which seems throughout its history to have been associated with religious cults.

89–90. Kay and Bedivere are frequently found in association in romances. The latter became a hermit after witnessing Arthur's final departure; the former was Arthur's foster-brother.

96. *forlond*: possibly the causeway linking the Mount to the mainland.

115. *But and yf*: 'unless'.

126. i.e. warming himself in front of the fire.

146. *see marke*: the high-water line.

158. *fyerst*: Malory has 'freysh'.

159. *mount of Arabé*: a mountain in Wales which is called *mons Aravius* by Geoffrey of Monmouth.

162. *retorned*: i.e. Arthur and the two knights.

VII

The poetic romance *Blancandin et l'Orgueilleuse d'Amour* was composed in France in the thirteenth century. At least three manuscripts of the poem survive, and a text was edited by H. Michelant, *Blancandin et l'Orgueilleuse d'Amour* (Paris, 1867). A French prose version was made from the poem and this is extant in two forms. The first is found in MS. 3577 of the Royal Library, Brussels, a manuscript which formed part of the Burgundian ducal library. This version has been divided into three books and is considerably abbreviated. The second is found in

MS. Bibliothèque nationale fr. 24, 371. It is this prose version which is closest to Caxton's translation and which has been used for comparison here. Caxton's translation is edited by L. Kellner, *Caxton's Blanchardyn and Eglantine c. 1489* (EETS, 1890).

As Caxton himself says, the book deals with 'the noble actes and fayttes of warre achyeved by a noble and victorious Prynce named Blanchardin, sone unto the Kynge of Fryse, for the love of a noble Pryncesse callyd Eglantyne . . . and of the grete adventures, labours, anguysshes and many other grete dyseases of theym bothe, tofore they myghte atteyne for to come to the fynall conclusion of their desired love'.

2. Eglantine's nickname in French is 'l'orguilleuse d'amours', a name she gained by refusing to listen to any offers of love, cf. ll. 332–4.

3. *knyght*: viz. the Knight of the Ferry.

11. *cause*: cf. 'cause de paour de faillir'.

14. *Love*: the Goddess of Love, cf. ll. 284–5.

35. Cf. 'par sa diligence enflambé de son ardant desir'; *taken wyth*: here 'excited by'.

36. *of her maystres*. The *of* has been carried over from the French, 'pres d'elle et de sa maitresse'.

46. Cf. 'ne savoit tenir sa maniere'; *in this byhalve*: 'in this matter', which is not found in the French.

50. *flowen*. It is difficult to account for the text's *fowghten*, for the French reads 'volassent en l'air'.

64–5. i.e. he took the direct road to Tormaday.

72–3. Cf. 'Quant elle polt parler dist'.

90–1. The sense is, 'should we take something as dishonourable which is not so?'

92. *be discovered nor knowen*: both used here in the sense 'to make known', see *OED*, *Discover*, *v.* 4, and *Know*, *v.* 13. The sense of the clause is 'have no fear that I should ever reveal it'.

96. The clumsy word-order has been taken over direct from the French. The sense is merely 'may God suffer me to live no longer unless . . .'.

101. *shal deye*: the subject pronoun *he* is understood, cf. No. I (*a*), l. 99, and note.

113–14. *wyth what peyne and grief that it was*: 'despite the pain and sorrow she endured'. The *she* (115), which is not found in the French, repeats the subject already given, *the proude pucelle in amours* (113). On the repetition of the subject see No. X, l. 184, and note.

142–3. The clumsiness of this sentence probably springs from a mistranslation. The French reads 'avec le trait qui des deux costez venoit l'un contre l'autre', where *trait* probably means 'impetus'. But *trait* can also mean 'flight of an arrow', and Caxton has understood it in this sense.

153. *swerde*. The sense demands 'spear' here (cf. French 'sa lance'), which has in fact been supplied in the margin in a sixteenth-century hand.

162. *man of the fayré*: a man from the land of the fays or fairies. In most medieval and Renaissance literature *fayré* refers to an imaginary land whose inhabitants had marvellous attributes. The concept received its finest expression in Spenser's *Faerie Queene*.

220–1. *cause movyng*: 'the cause which brings something about'; cf. the French 'cause motive'; *for* is here 'before, in front of'.

250–2. i.e., he was accompanied to his lodgings by the majority of the nobles who showed him as much honour as they could.

275–6. *that had syght wythin the towne*: 'that faced on to the town'.

280. *alle wayes*: 'nevertheless, still'.

288. *lovely*: 'amorous'.

291. *cause*: the French has *cas*, which gives better sense.

304. The subject of *cam* is Eglantine.

310. *God of Love*. Caxton usually interpreted *Amours* as Goddess of Love; but here the French text also has 'dieu d'amours'.

323. *knouleche*: as the French reads 'sachiez' it is best to understand *knouleche* as a verb meaning 'recognize, accept'.

331. *here*: it is possible that the final *e* has slipped down from *tak*[*e*]*n*; cf. No. XIV(*b*), ll. 141–2.

332. *Amours*. Caxton has not bothered to translate 'Amours'. In his texts there is often a variation between the French word and its English equivalent.

VIII

The story of the lovers Paris and Vienne became popular in the fourteenth century. Two versions are known, of which the later, used by Caxton for his translation, is a summarized account of the original story. Two texts of this version are extant: Bibliothèque nationale MS. fr. 20, 044 and Gerard Leeu's printed text of 1487. Both are very similar to Caxton's version, though neither is identical with it. See further J. Finlayson, 'The Source of Caxton's *Paris and Vienne*', *Philological Quarterly*, xlvi (1967), 130–5. Caxton's text is edited by M. Leach (EETS, 1957).

The story, as Caxton writes, is about Paris and Vienne, 'the whyche suffred many adversytees bycause of theyr true love or they coude enjoye the effect therof of eche other'.

4. On his previous visit the Duke of Burgundy's son had not seen Vienne, who had feigned sickness and had remained in her room. The Dauphin had therefore sent the suitor away in the hope that he might change Vienne's attitude by sending her for a time to prison.

18–19. Note the omission of the subject pronouns '[she] hath eten . . . and [I] have sworn'; cf. No. I (*a*), l. 99 and note.

21–2. i.e. you are certain to marry a great lady even if you do not marry my daughter.

31. *bycause*: here indicating purpose; see *OED*, *Because*, B. *conj*. 2.

43. The bishop plays a small part in the story, as he gives shelter and support to Paris and is Vienne's confessor.

68. *for you*: cf. 'pour l'amour de vous'.

71. Vienne is here referring to her lover Paris. She has promised him that she would marry nobody else but him.

95. *lyf of Vyenne*: this phrase, taken over directly from the French, means 'Vienne's condition'.

IX

A French version of Pierre Bersuire's *Ovidius Moralizatus* was made in the early fourteenth century. A shortened prose adaptation of this *Ovide moralisé* was made in the fifteenth century and is extant today in two manuscripts: Bibliothèque nationale fr. 137 and British Museum Royal MS. 17 E iv. Caxton's translation is based on a version represented by these two manuscripts and not, as was formerly thought, on Mansion's printed edition of 1484. See further H. Nørgaard, 'Sankt Ovid. Tekstligt og Billedmæssigt om Metamorfosernes Forvandling', *Fund og Forskning i det Kongelige Biblioteks Samlinger*, x (1963), 7–26. I have used the British Museum manuscript for purposes of comparison here.

Ovid was a popular author with medieval writers and his stories were frequently adapted and repeated; see L. P. Wilkinson, *Ovid Recalled*

(Cambridge, 1955). The tale reproduced here (*Metamorphoses*, vi. 424–674) was also used by Gower in his *Confessio Amantis*, v. 5551–6047, where it exemplifies rape, a subsidiary vice of avarice (see J. A. W. Bennett, *Selections from John Gower* (Oxford, 1968), pp. 80–93). It is also found in Chaucer's *Legend of Good Women*, 2228–93.

The last six books of Caxton's Ovid, in the original Pepys bequest to Magdalene College, Cambridge, were edited by S. Gaselee and H. F. B. Brett-Smith in *Ovyde hys booke of Methamorphose. Books X–XV* (Oxford, 1924). The first nine books came to light in 1965 and are now also in Magdalene. A facsimile of the whole work has been issued: *The Metamorphoses of Ovid translated by William Caxton 1480* (New York, 1968). This extract from the newly-found manuscript is printed by permission of the Master and Fellows of Magdalene.

2. *Phylomena and Prone*. Caxton has taken over the forms of these names direct from his French source; but following modern practice, I refer to the characters by their Latin names.

6. *This weddyng were*: cf. 'ces noepces furent'.

8. *Ledus the owle*: this is Caxton's translation of 'Ledus le chashuant'; the significance of Ledus is not clear. Ovid has *profanus bubo* (vi. 431–2).

10. *destynees*: the Fates, though Ovid (vi. 430) speaks of the Furies.

11. As usual in this edition, the chapter headings have been left out of the text. But in view of the special interest and unfamiliarity of this selection, the rubrics of this text are included in the notes. 'How Thereus, Kyng of Trace, espowsed Prone, doughtir of Kyng Pandeon of Athenes, and how aftir he enforced Phylomela [*corrected in MS.*], sustir of his wyf, and how he drewe her tongue out of her hed.'

12. *that*: 'when'.

19. The year of his birth and every following year a great feast was held to celebrate Itys's birthday.

34. *Thereus* [text *Theseus*], cf. l. 91. Caxton or the scribe has confused Tereus with the more famous Theseus.

38–9. i.e., after Philomela had been with Procne a day or two, Tereus would bring her back to Athens again when the wind was favourable.

42. *alle bare-heeded*: Fr. 'toute eschevelée', used of dishevelled hair usually signifying grief or fear in that person. The French may foreshadow Philomela's future sorrow; Caxton has rationalized the passage.

43–4. 'are insufficient to write or express . . .'.

49. *fawcons gentyl*: the position of the adjective is copied from the French 'faulcons gentilz ou laniers'. A *lanier* is a small falcon; it is not recorded in *OED*.

50. *flee at the ryver*: 'fly by the river-bank'; cf. 'aler en gibier ou en riviere'. The French has hunting in general ('gibier') or hunting beside a river for waterfowl ('riviere') to make it clear that she was expert at all types of hunting.

51. *purple bawdkyns*: cf. 'pourpres et baldequins'.

53–4. *she coude holde a scole.* Caxton has translated the French 'qu'elle en scavoit tenir escole' literally, though *escole* here has the sense 'counsel, advice'.

63–4. *But late . . . love*: not found in the French MSS.

69–70. *Ye had ben longe seen in Trace*: cf. 'ja piecha eussies esté en Trace', in which *ja piecha* means 'a long time ago'. So it is best to understand *seen* as a form of *sen/sin* 'ago', though it usually has a short vowel. But confusion of *sen* and *seen* is found in some senses and may have been extended to others; cf. *OED*, *Sen*, C. *conj.* 2.

83. *say* [text *sayde*]: the preterite is no doubt an anticipation of *sayde Thereus*; the French has 'vous dites'.

114–15. Sense demands a negative, which is found in the French. Translate: 'he thought he would go mad if he failed to satisfy his desire'.

115–16. *for it laye not in his myghte to leve hys corage*: cf. *car descouragier ne s'en povoit* 'he could not turn his thought from her'.

118. i.e., he concluded with himself.

119. *and for* [*to*] *take her.* In the French this clause goes with what precedes: 'Et pensoit par lui seul que par amours . . . et que par nuyt le convendroit a emblee mener ou par force [that by night he would lead her away secretly or by force]; mais pour telle chose faire il avoit peu de gens avec lui.' The central clause has been shortened and linked to what follows.

122. In every way he could; cf. 'en tout ce qu'il povoit'.

131. *poure occasyon*: translated literally from the French *povre occasion* 'a poor excuse'; cf. *OED*, *Occasion*, *sb.*[1] 2. b.

148. Cf. l. 179. The confusion of *th* and *d* is found in manuscripts as well as in printed books, so these examples do not prove that the text had been printed.

151–2. *by suche covenant and promyse that thou hast fyanced to me*: cf. 'par tel convenant que promys m'avez et fiancé'. Caxton has turned *promys* into a noun. *Fiance* in the sense 'to make a promise' is not recorded under *OED*, *Fiance*, *v.* 2, before 1592; Caxton also uses it in its more usual meaning 'to plight one's troth'.

156. *wente*: i.e., they went.

175. *more* [*th*]*an C tymes*: cf. 'plus de cent foys'.

186. *requyred of companye*: 'he demanded to have intercourse'.

189. *corrupte*: here the past tense, 'raped'.

191. *that he had don to* [*her*]. There is no parallel in the French.

192. *thenne that*: cf. 'affin que'.

195. The one is rape, the other is cutting out her tongue.

202. i.e., the old woman should provide Philomela with everything she needed.

212. *what she made*: 'what she was doing', cf. 'qu'elle faisoit'.

213–14. Where the French has two nouns 'de dueil et dangier de respondre', Caxton has changed the second into an adjective and so made the sentence clumsy. Translate 'he feigned sorrow and a reluctance to answer'.

241. *to werke in a curtyne*: cf. 'de faire une gourdine ouvrée'.

243 ff. Caxton has reorganized this passage. As a result its progression is less clear because of the ambiguity of the pronouns. In 'she knewe not what werke she made', the first *she* is the old woman, the second Philomela. The French has '. . . la vilaine avoit ses filles mys. Sy les prinst et desvuida et commenca par grant estude son œuvre telle comme il luy pleust. La vielle lui laissa faire et lui donna tout ce qu'elle pensa que a tel œuvre convenoit, fil vermeil, bleu, jaune, vert et d'autres couleurs. Mays riens ne congneut de ce que elle tyssoit. Et l'ouvrage lui embellissoit et moult lui plaisoit, car il estoit moult grief a faire.'

266. *And there as she laye in the wyndowe*: cf. 'de la ou elle estoit apuyé'.

267. *throughe*: cf. Fr. *entre* 'between', which gives better sense.

269 ff. The old woman is so sorry for Philomela that she will give her anything she wants except permission to leave the cottage. This provides another reason for her agreeing to send the tapestry. Caxton has confused the pronouns, as so frequently; the French reads 'en luy ottroyant tout ce qu'elle voulsist'.

272. The rubric reads: 'How Prone receyved the cortyne fro Phylomena, her suster, by which she knewe wher she was; and how she delyveryd her.'

284. *presente*: here the preterite.

294. *stelle*. This form could be emended to *stille*, but examples of the lowering of short *i* to *e* are found in the fifteenth century.

316. i.e., you are something closely resembling your father. The boy's likeness to his father suggests the form her revenge should take.

324. *it*: the French implies 'him', and Caxton may have confused the pronouns.

333–4. i.e., Itys.

342–3. *She broughte hym forth*: cf. 'Elle l'emmena'.

352. *what he ete and dyde*. Possibly Caxton did not understand the French and tried to make the best of a bad job. His translation may best be understood by taking *what* in the sense 'while', i.e. 'while he was eating and behaving (in this way)'. The French reads *quoy qu'il taillast ne mengast*, which may mean 'while he was cutting up and eating (the haunch)'.

357. The rubric reads: 'How Prone and Phylomena brought the heed of Ythis for to ete to his fader, and how they were transformed that one of them into a swalowe and that other into a nyghtyngale.'

364. *it bebledde hym*: i.e. the head caused him to bleed; the blow drew blood.

381. *Occy*: from French *occire* 'to kill'. Caxton has left it in its French form, possibly because it was more suggestive of the bird's cry; though as this form is also found in some medieval Latin versions of the tale, it may have been traditional.

382 ff. A *sens hystoryal* is provided for many of Ovid's stories. It is the allegorical or moral meaning of the tale, hence the *Ovide moralisé*.

393–4. *lapwynch or huppe whych is a fable byrde and a vylayne*: cf. 'huppecoppe ou huppe qui est oysel ort et villain'. The *huppe* is a hoopoe; but I can find no gloss for huppecoppe (which is not found in the Bibliothèque nationale MS.), though *coppe* may simply refer to the hoopoe's crest. Caxton probably did not know what it meant; his translation 'lapwing' was probably taken from Gower, from whom he borrowed on other occasions. *Ort* means 'dirty, wicked', which again Caxton may not have understood.

X

Accounts of the Trojan war were popular in the Middle Ages, and many of the west European nations traced their descent to one of the heroes who had participated in it. The medieval story of Troy was based on the Latin versions of Dares Phrygius and Dictys Cretensis. The story was soon retold in most European languages, and even in England there are several extant Middle English versions apart from Lydgate's *Troy-Book*, which remains the most famous. Continental versions likewise flourished, and in 1464 Raoul Lefèvre, chaplain to Duke Philip the Bold of Burgundy, made a French prose version based on the *Historia Troiana* of Guido delle Colonne. It is this version that Caxton used as a basis for his own translation. The book is of great interest as the first book printed in English. The French original was also issued from Caxton's press in Bruges a year or two after the English translation. I have collated Caxton's translation with the French printed text. It has been edited by H. O. Sommer, *The Recuyell of the Historyes of Troye* (London, 1894). The French quotations are taken from Caxton's edition of 1475–6.

In this medieval version the Greek gods are looked upon as kings of particular localities and they behave like medieval knights. Similarly, many of the mythological features are rationalized through allegory. Thus in this selection Medusa's serpent head symbolizes cunning and is not understood literally.

3. *See of Spaygne*. Cf. '. . . mer pour ce qu'il tenoit en sa subiection tous les rois habitans sur la mer d'Espaigne'.

16. *in feet*. Usually this phrase simply means 'in fact, indeed', see *OED*, *Feat, sb.* 7, but here it seems to be short for 'in feat of arms', i.e. with valiant deeds, noble exploits.

20. *temple* [*of*] *the goddesse*. Cf. 'temple de la deesse' and l. 126.

47–9. This sentence has been translated literally from the French, which accounts for the rather clumsy sentence-structure of the English. At first Neptune was going to seize Medusa by force; but as he reflected on her beauty another thought crossed his mind. In view of his comparative poverty and unattractiveness it would be impossible for him to win her love.

51. *matyer*. Caxton probably misread his original, which read *martire* 'martyrdom', a more suitable parallel to sorrow and pain.

56. *This is*. Neptune neither has sufficient wealth nor is sufficiently handsome to be a match for Medusa.

60. Love hurts a man through his eyes because he can see that his loved one is in all respects too good for him: cf. ll. 64–71.

62. *Wher I am, I put me oute*. The French reads 'Ou me suis je bouté?' According to Godefroy, s.v. *Bouter*, the reflexive *se bouter* means 'to enter or embark upon', so that the French could mean 'What have I embarked upon?' Otherwise it could mean something like 'Where am I placed? What position am I in?', for *bouter* can also mean 'to put, place'. Caxton misunderstood the sentence and perhaps was confused by Middle English *bout*(*e*) 'out, outside'. Translate 'I lose my self-possession'.

64. *reversid*. The French has 'plaine reverie'. Caxton possibly misread it.

67. *ataynt*: 'purpose, intent', see *OED*, *Attent, sb.* 3. The French printed text has *attente*, though some of the manuscripts have *entente*, the original reading. *OED* notes that it was just this confusion between *atente* and *entente* in Old French which gave rise to the meaning 'purpose, intent' for *attent* in Middle English.

85. *take pacience*: 'enjoy the hospitality of my house'. Cf. the French 'prendre la pacience de ma maison'. This sense is not recorded in *OED*, but see Godefroy, s.v. *Pacience*.

97. That is, Medusa does not wish to change her state of virginity for that of marriage.

117–19. Caxton has somewhat altered the French which reads 'pensez a ma priere et vous en venez avec moy. Je ne fay nulle doubte se vous y seiournez que la voulente ne vous change'. The confused text might have arisen in this rewriting, but it seems best to emend.

184. The *she* is repeated again in l. 186, the *comen* meaning 'having returned'. Caxton frequently repeats his subject after a participial clause; see L. Kellner, *Caxton's Blanchardyn and Eglantine, c. 1489* (EETS, 1890), p. xxxi. The first *she* is not found in the French.

191. *cyte of Naples*: cf. Fr. 'cité d'Apulie'. Caxton has tried to alter the Apulia in his source consistently to Naples, but he forgot occasionally as in l. 271.

193. *in his bruyt*. Translated literally from the French with the meaning 'at its height'.

195. *tempryen*. This word, which is not recorded in *OED*, has been taken direct from the French, which reads 'estoit en la verdeur de sa force temprienne'. The meaning of *tempryen strength* is 'youthful, precocious strength'. For the meaning of OF. *temprienne*, see Godefroy, s.v. *Temprif*.

The usual form in OF. was *temprieu*, and it is possible that Caxton did not understand the word here. Cf. l. 372.

228. *en*: a mistake for 'in', which may have been taken over from French *en* by Caxton, alternatively it may be a typographical anticipation of the *en-* of *entencion*.

261–4. The sense of this passage is a trifle clumsy, because Caxton mistranslated French *ou* 'or' as *where*, though he has tried to save the sentence by making some small insertions. The French reads 'entre Perseus et Meduse ou les Gorgonnes. Fortune qui Meduse avoit en chierté et en treshault degre de sa roe la deschevilla lors et consenti . . .'. Caxton's sentence is best understood by taking *where* in the sense 'in which' and *fortunat* in the sense 'blessed by fortune'.

310. i.e. 'we shall be remembered with honour everywhere'.

316. The French printed text reads 'tout le monde', but earlier manuscripts read 'chascun de vous', which is the meaning of 'Alle the world'. The verb is imperative.

329–30. Caxton has probably misunderstood his source once again. So it is not clear what he meant by 'putte us tofore the shame', though it probably has the sense 'our honour shall redeem the shame (we have endured today)'. The passage from the French is worth quoting in full: 'Les playes qui sont faittes en nostre honneur et sang nous approprions à aigreur et proesse. Nostre honneur nous chassera tout avant; la honte nous fera esvertuer.'

339. An example of Caxton using both singular (*his*) and plural (*her* 'their') pronouns to agree with 'eche man'. This lack of congruence is not found in the French.

366–7. *seconde bataylle*: i.e. the other division of Medusa's army.

368–9. *stronge partye for to maystrye*: cf. French 'eurent forte partie a maistrier', the meaning of which is 'had the greater advantage to conquer', i.e. were more likely to win the victory.

394. *Me* is a reduced form of *men*, used in the sense 'one'. On its use see T. A. Mustanoja, *Middle English Syntax* (Helsinki, 1960), pp. 219–23.

404. *rescuse*: 'aid, assistance'; Medusa retreated constantly to the banner (*theder to*) for aid.

426–7. The construction here is clumsy, but the sense is 'And everything went so badly on her side that . . .'.

XI

Numerous editions of *Æsop's Fables* were printed in the fifteenth century in Latin, French, German, and English versions. The *Romulus*, the medieval version of the fables, had been enlarged by the addition of other collections of fables or facetiae such as those of Avianus and Poggio. Not all versions added all the extra stories, so that there are many slight variations among editions. Caxton made his translation from a French version, almost certainly that by Julien Macho, the earliest extant copy of which was printed at Lyons in 1480. At the end of his version Caxton printed two further stories by Poggio and the fable given here as (*c*), which are not in any known version of Macho. R. H. Wilson, in 'The Poggiana in Caxton's *Esope*', *Philological Quarterly*, xxx (1951), 348–52, has shown that the two extra stories from Poggio are also found in the 1532 edition of Steinhöwel's German version. He has suggested that Caxton and the 1532 German edition both drew on a French printed version which is no longer extant. It is generally accepted that the tale of 'The Dean and the Parish Priest' was added by Caxton. His text is edited by R. T. Lenaghan, *Caxton's Æsop* (Cambridge, Mass., 1967).

(*a*) This fable is found also in Caxton's translation of *Jeu des Echecs*; see W. E. A. Axon (ed.), *Caxton's Game and Playe of the Chesse, 1474* (London, 1883), pp. 114–16; though in that version many details are omitted.

(*b*) 28–9. *for to have it made up myn owne werke*. One must assume that *it* is a superfluous object pronoun referring to *myn owne werke*. The Holy Ghost has been fulfilling the husband's marital obligations.

(*c*) 10. *annuel*: an annual priest or a priest who was paid to say prayers for a person's soul daily for a year. Occasionally it meant that the priest was to perform masses for the soul of the dead beneficiary once a year on the anniversary of his death. The former meaning is more probable here as there appears to be a contrast between a temporary and a permanent position, for a parish priest enjoyed the usufruct of a parish permanently.

19. *sowle preest*: a priest whose special function it was to pray for the souls of the dead; here probably to be understood as being the same as an annual priest (see preceding note).

XII

The *Liber de Ludo Scaccorum* of Jacobus de Cessolis, written in the late thirteenth or early fourteenth century, is based principally on *De*

Regimine Principum by Ægidius Romanus. About the middle of the fourteenth century, two French translations were made, one by Jean Ferron or Faron and the other by Jean de Vignay. A conflated version of these two translations was made and at least three manuscripts of this conflated text are extant, namely University of Chicago MS. 392 and Bibliothèque nationale MSS. fr. 2146 and 2471. C. Knowles, in 'Caxton and his two French Sources', *Modern Language Review*, xlix (1954), 417–23, has shown that Caxton used a text similar to the one found in these three manuscripts as well as the Latin original. I have collated the selection given here with the Chicago manuscript. Caxton's text was edited by W. E. A. Axon, *Caxton's Game and Playe of the Chesse, 1474* (London, 1883).

The *Liber* proved to be a very popular work and was translated into most European languages. The description of the chess pieces provided occasions for accounts of various classes that constituted medieval society and for a discussion of their duties. Room is also found for descriptions of some of the short-comings of each class, and the whole is embellished by exempla to illustrate the points made. The intention is didactic, though the vivid style and abundant exempla contribute to make it a colourful work of wide appeal.

1. The *alphyns*, dealt with in Book II, ch. iii, ought to be made in 'manere of juges syttynge in a chayer'; they are the bishops in chess.

20–1. The sin of gluttony forms the basis of the sermon in the Pardoner's Tale in *The Canterbury Tales*, which in its tone and choice of exempla is similar to this extract.

30. *Vitas Patrum*: *Lives of the Fathers*, traditionally ascribed to St. Jerome, a version of which Caxton himself translated from French into English; his version was published by de Worde (1495).

31. *gossibs*: here plural, meaning both the friend and his wife.

53–4. *the gate of the mouth*: the French has simply 'la bouche'.

57. *glotonsly*: *OED*, *Gluttonsly, adv.* 'gluttonously', accepts this form as genuine and compares such forms as *felonsli* and *vilainsly*. The latter occurs frequently in Caxton's works.

60. Cf. the French *Il convient que homme soit repeus et de terre et de mer*: 'It is fitting that man should be satisfied with what comes from land and sea.' Caxton's *fedde* should probably be understood in this way. The next sentence develops this thought, for its meaning is 'it is not difficult to

satisfy the necessities of the body, but it is difficult to satisfy the craving for exotic dishes'.

63. References to authorities were freely borrowed from other medieval books, so that many tend to be erroneous or only to represent their original in a very general way. The *Institutio Oratoria* of Quintilian, *c.* A.D. 35–100, was a standard textbook on rhetoric in the Middle Ages.

67. The *Pharsalia* (also known as *Bellum Civile*) of Lucan, A.D. 39–65, was noted for its rhetorical flourishes and was often imitated in the Middle Ages. It was typical of late medieval authors to claim that one sin was the mother of all vices: Caxton himself in his prologue to the *History of Troy* claimed that he wanted to 'eschewe slouthe and ydlenes whyche is moder and nourysshar of vyces'.

71. *joye*: the French has 'gloire'.

73. The *Catonis Disticha*, probably written in the first century A.D., were fathered on Cato (234–149 B.C.) because of his reputation for wisdom. Its use as a school text guaranteed its popularity. Caxton himself translated a version from French in 1483 and printed it; he also printed poetic versions of Burgh's *Parvus Cato* and *Magnus Cato*.

75. St. Augustine, Bishop of Hippo, 396–430, was one of the most prolific of the early fathers and one of the most frequently cited.

81. It is best to understand the clause beginning with *for* as part of the previous sentence, though in the French a new sentence begins here. *Car celuy qui a ostée la vertu de l'omme, la proesse languist, la gloire* . . ., 'Because the prowess of him who has dispensed with human virtue languishes, his glory . . .'.

84. *Basille le grant*: St. Basil the Great, *c.* 330–79, a famous Greek father whose extensive writings were well-known in the West.

84–6. The two clauses beginning 'late us take hede' and 'and we studye' form one sentence in the Latin and French texts, with the general sense 'In so far as we serve our stomachs through gluttony, we strive to make ourselves similar to beasts'. But Caxton has added 'lyke as we were dombe bestes and', and this has destroyed the original syntax. His English is best understood as forming two sentences. The phrase 'of the see' (l. 86) fits in awkwardly here, for the Latin of Jacobus de Cessolis which does not have a corresponding phrase clearly refers to beasts that live on land. But Chicago MS. 392 reads 'de mer'. An identical phrase, 'of the see', was added by Caxton at l. 92.

88–9. The *De Consolatione Philosophiae* of Boethius was a popular text in the Middle Ages and several English translations were made. Caxton printed Chaucer's version *c.* 1478. Boethius, *c.* 480–524, when imprisoned by Theodoric, whom he had served for many years, wrote the *Consolation.*

89–90. The French reads 'Home que delesse vertu delesse à estre homme et ne se puet transporter en nulle bonne condicion', which gives better sense than Caxton's translation and fits in better with the next sentence.

92 ff. Caxton's *How well*, an anglicized form of Dutch *hoewel*, means 'although'. Consequently it is necessary to put a comma after *overseen.* The sense is 'Although many important and learned people these days indulge in excess and fall into sin, do you not think it is a dangerous thing for a leader of a nation to drink so much that he loses control of himself?' In the French there are two separate sentences, the first one opening with *combien*, 'How many great men . . .'.

104. Ovid's *De Remedio Amoris* was a form of mock recantation for some of his earlier work. In the Middle Ages it was often taken at its face value.

106. There is no exact equivalent in the Book of Tobit, one of the biblical apocryphal books, but the phrase *blyndeth the syght* may refer to Tobit's own blindness.

112. This exemplum is related at greater length earlier in the *Game and Play of the Chess*; see Book III, ch. i. See also Gen. 9: 20–7.

115. For Lot see Gen. 19: 30–8.

118–19. *Boece reherceth that Crete* . . . The Latin has no equivalent to this sentence. Chicago MS. 392 has *Boece* as the subject of the subordinate clause as well as the subject of the main clause, though this is clearly a mistake; the French printed edition of 1504 reads 'Et Boesse raconte que Salamon qui estoit fleur . . .'. It seems likely that Caxton had a text like Chicago MS. 392 with *Boece* in both clauses and that he tried to correct this by substituting *Crete.* It is not clear who was meant, though perhaps it was Croesus who appears frequently in medieval literature as an example of excess (cf. *De Consolatione*, Book II, prosa 2).

127. See Matt. 14: 3–12.

129. The reference is to Belshazzar's feast as related in the Book of Daniel, ch. 5. In Daniel there is no reference to Tyrus, for which the Latin texts read Titus.

144. See Gen. 19: 1–8.

165. *and myght falle*: the subject is the masters of the horses, who, because their horses slow down for lack of proper feeding, fall into the hands of their enemies. Cf. the French 'ou faillent à leurs maistres en alentissant. Sique lez maistres cheent aucune foiz es mains de leurs ennemis'.

169. Chicago MS. 392 reads *la cité de palme*, though the French printed text of 1504 reads *la cité de pade*. The readings in the Latin texts differ, though most read *in Lombardie partibus apud Parmam*. Caxton's *Jene* is perhaps a correction for *palme*, by which he probably meant Genoa even though it is not in Lombardy.

186. A leaf of the Chicago manuscript is missing here, so that the rest of this extract cannot be compared with the French.

187–8. Compostela (NW. Spain), where St. James the Greater was venerated, was one of the most popular shrines in the Middle Ages.

214 ff. This passage is not found in the Latin texts.

216. The French printed edition of 1504 reads *Sainct Domin en Espagne*, so that the English *Saynt Donne* probably represents a misunderstanding on Caxton's part. The shrine meant was probably that of Santo Domingo de Silos.

224–5. *and began to crowe and to pasture*: possibly Caxton made a mistake in translating this passage, for the French printed edition of 1504 reads 'et commenca le coq a chanter et la geline a pasturer'.

XIII

One of the more popular of the vast compendia of knowledge so common in the Middle Ages was a French poem completed in 1245 entitled *Image du Monde*. Additions were constantly made to it, and finally a prose version was written. This work, which draws heavily on earlier Latin authors, discusses such things as the power of God, the geography of the world, and the lives of the philosophers. A manuscript of the French prose version was written in Bruges in 1464. This manuscript, now British Museum Royal MS. 19 A ix, was used by Caxton as a basis for his translation, which has been edited by O. H. Prior, *Caxton's Mirrour of the World* (EETS, 1913).

Virgil had the reputation of a magician throughout the Middle Ages—possibly because of his eighth eclogue and Book VI of the *Æneid*. See further D. Comparetti, *Vergil in the Middle Ages* (London, 1908), and J. W. Spargo, *Virgil the Necromancer* (Cambridge, Mass., 1934). Most of the stories given in this selection about Virgil are found commonly in the Middle Ages, and most had been popularized by Vincent of Beauvais in his *Speculum Historiale.*

2–3. *the vij sciences*: the *trivium* (grammar, rhetoric, and logic) and the *quadrivium* (arithmetic, music, geometry, and astronomy), which together made up the medieval seven liberal arts.

5. *Naples*: Caxton has changed the *Rome* of his source to *Naples* here and *Itaile* at l. 1. It may show his knowledge of other accounts of these stories, since they were usually associated with Naples, or he may have made the alteration because the city, the fly, and the horse are said to be still in Naples at l. 19. For the story of the fly see Spargo, op. cit., pp. 70–9.

14 ff. There is confusion about the egg and its relation to the city (Naples), since at ll. 14–16 the city is said to be founded on an egg, whereas at l. 19 the egg is said to be preserved in a cage in Naples. This confusion may reflect differing traditions about Naples, which was reputedly founded by Virgil, and to which he is said to have given a talisman in the shape of an egg. See further Spargo, pp. 87–99.

24. *nature*: 'female pudendum'; see *OED, Nature, sb.* 8.

25–6. *of th'Emperour and a grete lady*: the French reads less ambiguously 'fille d'empereur et de grant dame'.

27. *sklaundre and dysplaysir*: a reference to the common story about Virgil and the basket. Virgil fell in love with the Emperor's daughter, who pretended to reciprocate his love. An assignation was arranged, and Virgil was to reach her chamber by being pulled up to her window in a basket. But the lady pulled him only half-way up and left him stranded there to the amusement next day of the townsfolk. See Spargo, pp. 136–97, for various accounts and illustrations.

27–9. No one could light anyone else's taper from his own; everyone had to fetch fire direct from the Emperor's daughter.

63. Virgil's bones were traditionally said to be in Naples, where they continued to protect the city, as Virgil had done in his lifetime. Spargo, pp. 100–16, wonders whether this interest in the relics of Virgil may indicate that some venerated him as a saint.

92–3. *but he shold have knowleche therof*: there is nothing corresponding to this in the French.

97. *he*: earlier English uses *he* where today we use *one.*

102. *it is no maystrye*: 'it is not difficult'.

XIV

The *Book of the Knight of the Tower* was written in French by the Chevalier de la Tour Landry in the 1370s. It was translated into English for the first time by an anonymous translator during Henry VI's reign. Caxton completed his translation in 1483, though it was not published till 1484. It cannot be shown that he used the earlier English translation. Caxton's text is edited by M. Y. Offord (EETS, 1971), who has shown that, of the twenty-one extant manuscripts of the French original, MS. 9308 of the Royal Library, Brussels, is the one nearest to the manuscript Caxton used.

The book was a handbook of behaviour for the knight's daughters. He wrote a similar book for his sons, which has not survived. Books advising women or girls how to behave were common in the Middle Ages, perhaps the best-known being that written by the Ménagier of Paris; see E. Power, *Medieval People* (London, 1924). The knight explains to his daughters how a lady ought to behave, and then he lists the various things that a lady ought not to do. The general burden of the book is that women should be obedient and modest. The precepts are illustrated by stories drawn from the author's own experience and from the general stock of medieval exempla. Among the latter are many taken from the Bible.

(*a*) 24–5. *melancolyque*: the sense demands the meaning 'irascible' here; cf. *OED, Melancholy, sb.* 2.

66–7. It is typical of Caxton that he should not omit this story even though it depends upon a pun in French, for he omits smaller passages but rarely a complete story. Consequently he is forced to repeat the French containing the pun, without translating it. The confusion is between *sal* 'salt' and *saille*, the imperative of *sailler* 'to jump'.

(*b*) This story is the last in a group illustrating the theme of chastity. Some of the stories deal with incest (cf. l. 6), the others with adultery in general.

20. i.e., she who receives gifts sells herself to the giver.

53–4. The sense seems to be that the goodman's sight was confused by the half-light of dawn. Caxton may not have understood the French, which reads 'ce n'est que la nuit et le jour qui se bestournent'.

99. *lysynge*. One would have expected *losynge* or *lesynge*, but as *e*, *i*, and *y* are frequently confused by compositors, the form *lysynge* may perhaps be retained.

107. Possibly Caxton was going to shorten the text here as he does occasionally throughout the work, and so wrote *and brake bothe her legges*, which has no equivalent in the French, after *bete her*. Then he decided to include all the French, without correcting what he had already written.

112. The emendation to *commaundement*, the reading in the French, makes better sense than *covenaunt*. Caxton or the compositor may have been confused by the occurrence of *covenaunt* a little earlier.

118. *she myght not chastyse her*: cf. the French *elle ne s'en voulut nullement chastier* 'she simply would not mend her ways'.

142 ff. The greater the sin the more power the Devil has over the sinners. As he was a priest and she a married woman, the sin was in this case particularly heinous. Consequently they were almost completely within the Devil's power.

146 f. This does not refer specifically to this story, but to the whole group of stories, cf. l. 6.

XV

The collection of saints' lives known as the *Golden Legend* (*Legenda Aurea*) was composed by Jacobus de Voragine, an archbishop of Genoa, in the late thirteenth century. The collection, which achieved immediate popularity, contains a summary of hagiographic material current in medieval Europe. It was translated into French and from this an English translation was made in the first half of the fifteenth century. Several manuscripts of this earlier English version are extant. Although he had a copy of this version, Caxton decided to make a translation of the French himself, and he incorporated material drawn from the Latin and earlier English texts. The relationship of Caxton's translation to these earlier versions has been investigated by Pierce Butler in *Legenda Aurea—Légende dorée—Golden Legend* (Baltimore, 1899). Butler suggested that the French text in British Museum Stowe MSS. 50 and 51 was very close to the one used by Caxton. Caxton's translation was reprinted by William Morris at the Kelmscott Press (3 vols., London, 1892).

The legend of St. Ursula has always been closely associated with Cologne. It is possible that the legend arose through a fourth- or fifth-century inscription in the church of St. Ursula at Cologne. This inscription records that an old basilica was restored by Clematius near the spot where holy virgins had shed their blood for the faith. By the ninth century the number of virgins had grown to thousands, and the legend seemed to be authenticated in 1106 by the discovery of a cemetery near

St. Ursula's. See further W. Levison, *Das Werden der Ursula-Legende* (Cologne, 1928).

19. Not only do some of the earlier English MSS. read *he* here, but also the Stowe MS. has 'elle . . . fist tant à son pere qu'il se consentit au mariage'. So probably *she* is a typographical error for *he*. The *she* . . . *dyd soo moche*, 'she exerted her influence to such an extent', presupposes that it will be the father who will be influenced and who will agree to the marriage. The *he* of ll. 20 and 21 refers to the King of England. The emendation of *she* to *he* (in l. 19) makes the *to her fader* clumsy (one would expect *to him*), but this is also the reading in the French.

28. The subject of *commaunded* is not expressed and could be either the 'yonglyng' or his father; but it is most likely the latter.

29 ff. This sentence is clumsy not only because Caxton repeats *ordeyned*, but also because the construction with *that* after the first *ordeyned* is incomplete and there is a different construction after the second *ordeyned*. The general sense is 'The virgin's father appointed some worthy men to join their company in order to serve his beloved daughter and the other virgins, who were in need of protection and support'.

41. *had sygnefyed*. The verb is used intransitively here.

41. *she*: the repetition of the subject is not uncommon in Caxton; see No. X, l. 184, and cf. *they* (l. 122).

45. An emendation to *her* (from *his*) is best, for it is unlikely that 'her lytel sone' would already have a son of his own. Caxton frequently confuses his pronouns. Stowe MS. 51 reads 'd'un sien filz'.

89 f. Caxton has two main verbs *sawe* . . . *doubted* without a co-ordinating conjunction. The sense must be 'seeing this great company of virgins, they feared . . .'.

116 f. The versions differ a little here. Stowe MS. 51 reads 'et vint avec elle à Florence. Sa petite seur estoit ja crestienne et avec l'evesque Clement'.

143. *reason of the tyme*: 'dictates of chronology'.

144. Constantinople was founded by the Emperor Constantine and formally dedicated on 11 May 330. Sicily, originally part of the Roman Empire, was made one of the provinces of Italy by Constantine; it was subsequently conquered by the Vandals under Gaiseric, by Belisarius, by the Arabs, and finally by the Normans in the eleventh century. Not till then could Sicily be regarded as a separate kingdom, though it enjoyed considerable independence under most of its masters.

148. Marcian was the Eastern Emperor from 450 to 457.

153–7. This passage, which has no equivalent in the Stowe MS., was evidently added by Caxton. He is known to have visited Cologne in 1471 where he almost certainly learned the art of printing. For additions made by Caxton to the *Golden Legend* see Sister M. Jeremy, 'Caxton's Original Additions to the *Legenda Aurea*', *Modern Language Notes*, lxiv (1949), 259–61.

156. *xxvj*^{m}: twenty-six thousand.

163. *matyns*: the first of the canonical offices sung in the early hours of the morning.

165. *seeynge alle the monkes*: 'in the view of all the monks'.

192–6. This passage has no equivalent in the Stowe MS.

XVI

Caxton translated the *Order of Chivalry* from a French version of Ramon Lull's *Le Libre del Orde de Cavayleria*, which laid down how a knight ought to behave, and offered a symbolic interpretation of the various pieces of a knight's equipment. To his translation (ed. A. T. P. Byles, EETS, 1926) Caxton added this epilogue, one of the best specimens of his own composition.

On the revival of chivalry in the late Middle Ages and the part played in this by Caxton, see A. B. Ferguson, *The Indian Summer of English Chivalry* (Durham, N.C., 1960).

3. The squire who requested the translation has not been identified.

3–4. Caxton set up his printing-press at the sign of the Red Pale within the precincts of Westminster Abbey.

7. Caxton stresses throughout his translation that chivalry is meant for men of noble birth alone; see Byles, op. cit., p. xxxix.

9. No previous editor has included a *not* here, but the sentence does not make adequate sense without it. Caxton is stressing that chivalry has been forgotten in recent times (*these late dayes*), for modern knights do not follow the precepts set out in the *Order of Chivalry*.

15. Brenius and Belynus were brothers who were thought to have reigned in Britain before the birth of Christ. According to Higden's *Polychronicon* they quarrelled at first, but afterwards made peace through their mother's agency. Subsequently they conquered France and Germany and besieged Rome. The two brothers are also mentioned in the text of Malory as

printed by Caxton (cf. E. Vinaver, *The Works of Sir Thomas Malory* (Oxford, 1967), p. 188). Caxton could have taken his account from either source, for 'th'old hystoryes of the Romayns' is probably only a general reference.

19–20. Caxton printed Malory's *Le Morte d'Arthur* in 1485; see Nos. I (*b*) and VI above.

22. *large volumes*: cf. No. I (*b*), ll. 40, 67–70. *world*: 'marvel, wonder', see *OED, World, sb.* 19. c.; thus *thyng incredyble to byleve* is the second part of a doublet.

28. The *Roman de Perceforet*, written in the thirteenth century, deals with England in pre-Arthurian times, though it was influenced by the Arthurian cycle. Its hero, an Indian, epitomizes the chivalric ideal. A prose adaptation of this romance was made by David Aubert in 1459–60; and the work is said to have been popular at the court of the Dukes of Burgundy.

30 *latter dayes*: after 1066 (the Conquest), but excluding more recent times. Caxton was probably thinking of the period ending with Henry V's death in 1422, after which things went badly for the English in France.

31. Richard I (1189–99) was famous for his expeditions to the Holy Land. He was particularly remembered at this period because attempts to launch another crusade were being made.

32. Edward I (1272–1307) was famous for his wars against the Welsh and Scots. Edward III (1327–77) was the victor of Crécy. Of his sons the Black Prince was noted for his chivalry and his victory at Poitiers. Edward's other sons were John of Gaunt, Thomas of Woodstock, Edmund of Langley (all mentioned in No. II above), and Lionel of Antwerp.

33. Robert Knolles commanded a band of freebooters and later served under the Black Prince. John Hawkwood had a colourful career at the head of a company of freebooters in France and Italy. John Chandos served in the Hundred Years' War and was a friend of the Black Prince. He is portrayed as a noble knight in Froissart.

34. Caxton's text has *Manuy*, but Gauthier's surname usually appears as Mauny or Manny. He served under Edward III in the Hundred Years' War and is portrayed in Froissart as an ideal knight.

34. Jean Froissart (*c*. 1337–1410), poet, and historian of the Hundred Years' War; his *Chronicles* describe not only the warfare and battles of

the fourteenth century, but also life and manners in several countries in western Europe. He had visited England where he was well received. He admired chivalry, the knightly class, and generosity, the virtues that Caxton himself praises. The famous knights mentioned by Caxton (with the exception of Richard I) figure prominently in the *Chronicles*, and it is probable that Caxton had just read this work. Possibly he even intended to translate and print it. An English translation was made by Lord Berners and printed by Pynson in 1523–5.

35. Henry V (1413–22), the victor at Agincourt, had three brothers: Thomas, Duke of Clarence, John, Duke of Bedford, and Humphrey, Duke of Gloucester. Thomas de Montacute or Montagu, fourth Earl of Salisbury, fought at Agincourt.

64. This is Richard III (1483–5).

GLOSSARY

In the Glossary *y* is treated alphabetically as *i*, except initially. There are many variations in Caxton's orthography, but though cross-references are not normally provided, the reader should have no difficulty in finding a word. There is, however, considerable variation in the use of initial *in-/im-/em-/en-*, and in the use of *e/y/i*. Where a word differs from its modern equivalent only in spelling, it is not included unless the form might confuse the reader. The Glossary includes only obsolete words or meanings; words glossed in the Notes are not repeated here.

a, an, on.
abandon, hand over, allow.
abasshe, abaysshe, be amazed, confounded.
abhomynable, horrible.
abyde, wait for; continue; remain; **~ by,** remain faithful to.
able, make capable, enable.
above, beside, in addition to.
abusyon, perversion, deceit.
accord, allow, give permission; make an agreement.
accordyng, suitable.
achauffid, passionately heated.
acoynt, become known, acquainted.
admonest, exhort, admonish; **-ment,** warning.
adoo, have ~, have intercourse.
adoubed, equipped, arrayed.
adoulce, mollify, soothe.
adresse, prepare; pass on; **~ to,** make one's way towards, attack.
adventure, happening, incident; **by ~,** by chance; **in an evyl ~,** by an unfortunate chance; **sette it in ~,** put it to the test.
advertysed, informed.
advis, *n.* intention, plan; *vb.* reflect, consider.
aferde, afraid, frightened.
affections, lust.
affynyte, alliance, association.
affraye, terrify.
afore, in front of.
after, following, according to; **~ that,** when.
afterdele, disadvantage.
aftirst, rear.
agaynsaye, deny, refuse.
agrevyd, physically afflicted.
al, entirely.
alyaunce, union through love.
also, as.
amblere, an ambling horse.
amended, cured, healed.
amerveyled, amazed.
amyable, causing pleasure.
amours, love.
anguyssh, severe pain; **-ous,** tormenting.
annoye, vexation, grief; troublesomeness.
anon, immediately.
aourned, decorated, ornamented.
apayed, satisfied, content.
apayringe, deterioration, damage.
apoynte, come to terms; prepare; **-ment,** agreement, pact.
appareylle, equip, arm; prepare.
appel, accuse of a crime.
apperceyve, observe, notice.
apperteyn, be fitting.
appertisement, clear evidence, display.
appetite, desire, inclination.
apposite, opposite, contrary.

ar, er, before.
araged, enraged.
aray, order, rank.
arayed, dressed, armed; decorated.
araught, struck, reached.
areste, stay, commandeer.
arette, impute.
armehooles, armpits.
arson, saddle-bow.
aslepe, numb.
assayllyng, assaults.
assertryce, advocate (fem.).
asseured, confident, bold.
assoylle, pardon, grant absolution to.
assoted, out of control of one's senses.
astate, rank, order; condition.
astoned, astonyed, amazed, paralysed.
astrologyen, astrologer.
aswage, mollify, soothe.
aswoune, in a swoon.
attayne, strike, hit.
attempryd, controlled, even-tempered.
auctorite, power.
auncyent, former, olden; **-ly,** in former times.
avale, descend; lower, take down.
avauntage, opportunity.
awayte on, pay court to.

bague, ring, brooch.
bayne, bath.
banyer, banner.
barbares, barbarians.
barbycan, fortified gate.
barre, gate.
bawdkyns, rich embroidered cloth, brocade.
bawme, potion.
beal, beautiful.
bebledde, made bloody.
become, come to pass.
behavyng, conduct, behaviour.
behavoure, kepe ~, behave in an appropriate manner.
behelde, belonged.
behoveful, necessary.
bekynge, toasting, baking.
belue, wild beast, monster.
benefyce, protection, advantage.
benefyced, endowed with a benefice.
beneurte, happiness.
benyvolence, joy, happiness.
bent, inclined, ready.
bepysse, saturate with urine.
bespringe, attack.
bestourne, distract, deceive.
bete, strike, maul.
bethink, consider, decide.
bewray, disclose, reveal.
by, through.
bycause, ~ of, ~ that, because.
bienfayt, noble deed.
byheste, londe of ~, promised land.
byshote, excreted.
blamyng, bringing into discredit.
bodyly, in physical form.
borough, burghe, hamlet, village.
bourd, jest.
bourgeyses, merchants' wives.
bowellys, intestines.
breche, breeches; **-les,** without trousers.
brede, breadth.
breke, do violence to.
brenne, burn.
bretheren, members of the livery companies, leading citizens.
bryng, accompany, escort.
broche, *n.* skewer, spit; *vb.* impale.
bruyauntly, noisily.
bruyt, noise, clamour.
brutyssh, rude, uncultured.
buscage, thicket, grove.
busyne, trumpet.
but yf, unless.

caas, deed; **in ~ that,** in the event of; **to the ~ requyred,** necessary in the matter.
caytyf, wretch, fool.
careful, sorrowful.
casuall, accidental.
cause, matter.
cautele, trickery, guile.
cercle, band encircling a helmet.
certes, indeed.
chambre, capital, metropolis.
chambrier, chambermaid.
chapiter, meeting-place.
charge, care, duty.

chargid, filled; sodden.
chauffed, passionately heated.
chaunged, of a different colour, pale.
chere, provisions, food; entertainment; **what ~?,** How are you?; **make good ~,** make merry.
chydar, trouble-maker.
chierte, in ~, affectionately.
chyvalrye, prowess in war; knights; **-ous,** valiant, doughty.
chuse, pick out, see.
cyrurgyen, surgeon.
clenly, chastely.
clerke, scholar.
cleve under, stick to, adhere to.
cloistre, monastery.
clope, blow.
close fro, cut off.
closed, enclosed, set; imprisoned.
closure, cover, case.
cogges, ships (used for military expeditions).
colyons, testicles.
coloure, by the ~ of, under the pretence of.
comand, commend, commit, entrust.
come, hand down; **~ aboute,** throng round; **~ to,** befall; **~ evyl to passe,** turn out badly; **~ oute,** become common knowledge.
comynycacion, conversation, talk.
comynyng, conversation, talk.
comyns, common people.
commyse, entrust.
commun wele, state, community.
compass, set, devise.
competent, suitable, proper.
composicion, agreement, contract.
composynge, composition, written form.
compryse, include, contain.
compte, make a reckoning.
comunly, frequently.
conceyve, understand.
conclucion, decision.
condicions, nature, manners, behaviour.
conduyte, guidance; leadership; bodily passage.
confisqued, confiscated.
confound ded, die a violent death.
confused, discomfitted.
confusion, discomfiture.
conne, couthe, be able, know.
connyng, intelligence, skill.
conservatryce, female conservator or preserver.
conservynge, preservation.
constantly, with constancy, firmly.
constitue, appoint.
contemplacyon, religious musing, devout meditation; view, sight.
corage, *n.* heart, spirit; *vb.* take courage, embolden.
cordaylle, cordage, ship's tackle.
coronal, coronet.
cosyn, used as a familiar form of address; kinsman.
cotydyan, daily.
coulevre, coleuver, snake.
counte, story, tale.
countour, prison.
courbed, crooked, bent.
covenable, appropriate, convenient.
covetyse, inordinate desire for mortal rank.
crafte, skill, art; *pl.* members of a profession or trade.
crye, *n.* proclamation; *vb.* appoint, proclaim.
crochette, projecting adornment of a helmet.
cronyke, chronicle.
crueltee, cruel deed.
culpe, blame; **-able,** guilty.
cultyveresse, cultivator (fem.).
curate, parson of a parish.
cure, spiritual charge; **duty**; care, anxiety.
cursyd, wretched.
curtyne, tapestry, hanging.
curtoys, graciously polite.
curtosye, courtly behaviour.
cusse, cussynge, kiss.

damoyselle, lady.
dampned, condemned.
Dan, a title, often used when addressing someone in orders.
dangerously, gravely, seriously.
dasewed, dimmed, dulled.
daunt, conquer.

debate, *n.* quarrel, contention; *vb.* deliberate upon.
debonair, gracious, courteous; **-ly,** graciously; **-te,** gentleness, kindness.
decore, adorn, embellish.
defaute, fault, mistake.
defensable, fit for defensive actions; **-ly,** armed sufficiently to defend oneself.
deffend, forbid, prohibit; refuse, withhold; **-ence,** prohibition.
deffye, challenge.
defowl, rape; shamefully ill-treat.
degree, rank.
delybered, resolved, determined.
delices, delights.
delynge, contriving.
deme, think.
demene, handle, treat.
depart, distribute; **~ with,** spend; **-ment, -yng,** departure.
depe, extensive.
depresse, vanquish, crush.
dere, grieve, afflict.
derke, grow dark, dim.
descende, dismount; set sail.
descomfyte, routed; **-ed,** worsted; **-ure,** defeat, rout.
descovere, reveal, explain; **-ed,** uncovered, bare, naked.
descryve, describe.
desyryng, eager.
desloyal, false, unfaithful.
desmaylled, deprived of pieces of mail.
despite, indignation, anger; **-eous,** contemptuous, opprobrious.
despoylle, plunder, rob.
despoyllis, plunder, booty.
determine, judge.
detrench, cut in pieces.
devaunce, anticipate, forestall.
devyse, suggest, plan.
devyses, conversation, talk.
devoyre, duty; endeavour, effort.
diffame, dishonour, disgrace.
diffinityf, final, irrevocable.
dyght, prepare.
digne, worthy.
dygnyte, rank, office.
dylygence, do my trewe ~, apply myself to the utmost.
disancre, weigh anchor.
discomforted, disconsolate.
dyscrete, prudent.
disease, discomfort, hardship.
dyseased, troubled, afflicted.
disfygured, deformed.
dismesurable, immoderate; **-ly,** proudly.
dysobeysaunt, disobedient.
disordinate, unrestrained, immoral.
disordred, corrupted.
dispairly, in a manner causing despair.
dysplaysir, grief, sorrow.
displease, give offence.
dysporte, *n.* pastime, diversion; *vb.* entertain, amuse oneself.
dysposed, evyl ~, in a bad physical condition.
dyspourveyed, deprived.
dispreyse, blame, disparage.
dyssencyon, quarrel.
dyssymyl, dissimulate.
distemperance, disorder.
distourblyng, trouble.
distressid, harassed, overwhelmed.
disworshiped, dishonoured.
dyuturnyte, duration.
dyvulgacion, publication.
doctryne, religious instruction.
dolour, grief, suffering, pain; **-ly,** sorrowfully.
Dolphyn, Dauphin.
dommage, misfortune; **-eous,** grievous, harmful.
doo, cause to do; **had to ~,** had intercourse; **not to ~,** to have no business; **~ after,** act in accordance with; **~ wel,** behave valiantly; **to ~ withall,** have need of something.
doubt, *vb.* fear.
doubte, make no ~, have no fear.
dow, wring.
drawe, make one's way; **~ oute,** translate; **~ to that parte, theder,** advance in that direction.
dresse, prepare, get armed.
drynke dronke, drink oneself into a drunken state.
droef, drove.
dromoundes, fast ships.
dronkenship, drunkenness.

dure, last, endure.
duresse, hardness, stubbornness.
dwell, remain.

ease, take ~, relax.
edefye, build.
egal, equal, like.
eygre, bitter, fierce.
eythre, both.
elders, forefathers, ancestors.
embassade, deputation.
eme, uncle.
empesshe, hinder, prevent.
emprayntе, assault, charge.
emprynt, *vb.* print.
empryse, distinction, glory.
enameled, ornamented.
enbaysshement, confusion, shame.
enchace, drive away.
encharge, drive away.
enclyne, bow; **-ed,** facing, directed towards.
enclose, hide.
encreace, be enlarged.
ende, to th' ~ that, in order that; **at the last ~,** finally.
endevoyre, exert oneself.
endlong and overthwart, from end to end.
enduced, accustomed, skilled.
enele, anoint.
enflamyng, passionate.
enforce, constrain, oblige; strive; rape; encourage.
engendre, give birth to, produce; spring, develop.
engyne, device, plan; talent, genius.
englissh, translate into English.
enhaunce, raise, lift.
ennoblysshed, distinguished by the gift of.
enprynte, sette in ~, print.
enpryse, undertake.
enquyre, make an investigation.
ensample, illustrative story.
enseal, seal up.
enseigne, show, instruct.
enserche, seek out, make inquiry.
enspyred, suggested by divine agency.
entech, infect.
entencion, desire.
entendement, faculty of understanding, mind; will, purpose.
entent, intend.
ententyvely, earnestly, thoughtfully.
entermete, interfere; play.
enterpryse, *n.* daring spirit; *vb.* take upon oneself, undertake.
entraylles, intestines.
entre, *n.* beginning; entrance; *vb.* penetrate.
entretene, maintain, support.
envyronne, surround.
erthe, world; **at ~,** on the ground; **in ~,** in the world.
eschauffe, inflame, incite.
escrye, call upon, invoke.
espece, kind.
especiall, particularly.
espousailles, marriage.
esprise, enkindle, impassion.
esvertue, embolden.
everych, each one, everybody.
evydently, so as to be clearly visible.
evyl, *n.* wickedness; *adj.* wicked, unfortunate; *adv.* unfortunately.
evyll wylle, malice, malevolence.
exaltacyon, advancement, glory.
ex(c)ersyse, *n.* use; *vb.* practise.
excersyte, practice; army.
excitacion, instigation.
excluded, without experience of.
excusacion, excuse.
exhortyng, exhortation, address.
experyment, experience.
exploуte, succeed; exert oneself.
expose, risk, imperil.

fable, fictitious.
fayll, be extinguished.
fayn, take pleasure from.
fayr, courteously.
fayt, deed; **~ of warre,** warlike action.
falle, *n.* condition; *vb.* befall, take place.
false, break, violate.
faste, diligently; firmly.
fatte, greasy.
feawte, fealty, feudal obligation.
feble, enfeeble.
feyth, fidelity.

fel, cruel, savage; angry, enraged.
felde, battlefield, lists.
fele, be conscious, perceive; smell.
felon, wicked, base; **-ie,** crime.
ferdful, terrifying.
ferme, sette to ~, sell the privileges of raising taxes.
fermly, resolutely.
ferocyte, fierceness.
ferre, far.
fervently, earnestly, passionately.
fette, fetched.
fyerste, fierceness, high spirits.
fyl, befell, arose.
fyn, pure, refined.
fynably, finally.
fyngres, poynte me wyth ~, point at me in scorn.
flateryng, flattery.
flessly, carnally; **have to do ~,** have intercourse.
flytteryd, was scattered.
floytyng, singing in flute-like tones, flattery.
floures, adornments in shape of flowers on helmet.
folye, wickedness; **-ly,** foolishly.
foole, foolish.
foot, put under ~, conquer.
for, before, in front of.
force, *n.* power, might; *vb.* rape.
forfayt, misdeed, crime.
forgetenes, forgetfulness.
foryeve, forgive.
forlonge way, little, shortly.
forme, sette in ~, set up in type.
formest, front.
forseen that, provided that.
forth, furthermore.
fortune, befall.
forward, agreement.
founden, succeeded, brought about.
fowle, poor, shameful.
fraye, assault, attack.
fraunchyse, *n.* freedom, legal immunity; *vb.* enfranchise, liberate.
fryvolle, trifle.
fro, from.
froward, adverse, unfavourable.
furnysshe, accomplish, provide.
furour, rage, anger.

gaderynge, composition, collection of material.
gaynsaye, deny, refuse.
garnyson, garrison.
garnyssh, adorn, decorate; equip.
gendre, kinsman, son-in-law.
genytours, testicles.
gente, comely, elegant.
gentylmen, men of noble rank.
gentylness, good breeding, fine manners.
gete, capture.
give over, abandon.
glayve, lance, spear.
glose, interpret.
gloton, rascal (as a term of reproach).
goo, ~ togydre, join in combat; **~ aback,** retreat.
good, sufficient.
goode, property, possessions; *pl.* benefits.
goodman, husband, head of household.
goodwife, mistress of the house.
gossip, friend, acquaintance.
governaunce, control, rule.
graunte, admit, acknowledge.
gree, in ~, in good part, with equanimity.
grepe, gripped.
grete, large, big.
grymly, hideous, terrible.
grynne, snare.
grythe, protection, asylum.
grutche, complain.
guaryssh, cure, heal.

habergeon, sleeveless coat of mail, hauberk.
halowe, observe solemnly.
halse, embrace.
happe, befall.
hard, with difficulty, painfully.
hardy, bold; **-ly,** courageously; **-nesse,** boldness, courage.
harnoys, armament, gear.
haste, cause to move quickly.
hasty, irascible, rash; **-ly,** soon.
hauberke, coat of mail.
haultayn, loud, violent.
haultesse, pride, nobility.

haunt, frequent, use; live; **-yse,** practice.
have, I may ones ~ hym, I may deal him one blow.
havoyre, possessions, wealth.
heye, noble, leading; **-ly,** nobly, with pride.
heyghte, an ~, to a great height.
henge, hanged, was hanging.
herberowe, *n.* inn; *vb.* lodge, give shelter to.
here withal, at that.
hete, anger, passion.
hevyness, sorrow, misfortune.
hystoryal, historical.
historyes, stories, accounts.
holde, putte in ~, imprisoned.
holde, hold (land on feudal terms); keep to; **~ wel with,** approve of; **~ not on me,** is not my fault; **holden,** reputed, considered.
hole, uninjured.
honeste, honour, reputation; **-ly,** worthily, in a seemly manner.
honourably, with respect.
hoos, hoarse.
hope, expect.
horsbrede, bread made of beans or bran given to horses.
horsloof, loaf of horse-bread.
hosteler, innkeeper.
how be it, although.
howlyng, prolonged outcry.
humanyte, courtesy, politeness.
humylieng, humiliation.
hurte, trouble, distress.
husbondman, householder.

impetre, obtain by entreaty.
incontynent, immediately; **-ly,** immediately.
inconvenytys, hardships, harms.
infinyte, unlimited number.
infyrmyte, frailty.
infortune, misfortune.
inowh, sufficiently, enough.
institutes, established laws, customs.

jentyl, noble, of high birth.
jeopardyes, perils, dangers.
joyous, cheerful.
journeye, day's march.
jovencell, young man.
justes of pees, tournament(s).

kepe, preserve oneself; defend; **~ wel,** look after oneself.
kertyl, tunic, coat.
kynne, with one her ~, with one of her blood-relations.

labouryng, rolling heavily at sea.
lack, be wanting.
lang, long, belong to.
languissh, lose its vigour.
largely, copiously, extensively; in great numbers.
lass, diminish, decrease.
late, recently.
latter, more recent.
lecture, reading.
leye, ~ doun, assuage, dispel; **~ open,** expose.
lepe, leapt.
lesynge, lie.
lette, hinder, prevent; **-yng,** hindrance.
lettred, educated.
leve, cease to do something; abandon.
lybertees, privileges, immunities.
lichorous, rich, dainty.
lyeutenaunt, viceregent, representative.
lyght, nimble; **-ly,** nimbly.
lignage, lineage; family; royal family.
lysynge, loss.
lyteral, written.
lock, allure, entice.
longe, for a long time.
longynge, belonging to, appertaining to.
lore, learning; teaching.
lose, set free; cause to be lost.
lothly, loathsome.
lupaert, leopard.
lusty, healthy, vigorous.
luxurye, lasciviousness.

maylles, metal rings of a chainmail.
maynten, affirm; observe; conduct oneself.

maystresse, companion; keeper.
make, bring it about.
malade, sick person, invalid; **-ie,** sickness, disease.
malancolye, state of dejection.
male, bag.
malefayt, wicked deed.
malyce, evil, wickedness.
manace, threat.
manere, usage, practice; **all ~,** all sorts.
manhode, manliness, courage.
manyere, behaviour, bearing; **held ~,** acted civilly.
mater, dispute, disagreement.
matte, confounded, worsted.
medle, *n.* fight, engagement; **~ wyth,** *vb.* deal with, busy oneself with.
medlynges, strife, ravaging.
meyne, household, servants.
mekyng, humbling, humiliation.
melancolyque, moody, prone to anger.
membrers engendreurs, organs of procreation.
memorye, memorial; **oute of ~,** beside oneself.
mene, humble, lower-class.
mene, meen, by the ~ of, through the medium of; **had founde the ~,** had managed.
merytoryously, deservedly.
merveylle, was no ~, it was not surprising; **-ous,** astonishing, surprising; **-ously,** so as to excite wonder.
meschyef, trouble, distress; **at a grete ~,** in a sorry plight.
mesease, distress, affliction.
messagers, messengers.
messe, dish.
mesure, *vb.* restrain; *n.* moderation; **out of ~,** immoderate.
mete, food.
mete, suitable.
meure, mature, responsible.
meve, be enraged; attack.
myddes, middle.
mykle, much, great.
myllenes, mylnes, mills.
mynystre, administer.
mynussh, diminish.
mysadventure, bad luck, misfortune.
myschaunt, wicked, base.
myscreaunte, heretic, pagan.
mysfal, *n.* misfortune; **~ to,** *vb.* turn out badly for.
mysgoverned, unruly, unrestrained.
myspende, waste.
myssaye, abuse, slander.
moche, very; **for as ~ as,** because; **in so ~ as,** with the result that; **in so ~ that,** to such an extent that; **dyde so ~,** exerted oneself to such an extent.
mocquerye, scorn, absurdity.
moderat, moderated.
moeve, restrain.
moyen, middle, centre.
molestacyons, cause of annoyance.
mommery, mumming.
monarchye, rule, sovereignty.
monycyon, warning.
monoye, wealth, possessions.
moo, more.
mortall, fatal; **-ly,** so as to cause death.
motion, instigation.
mount, increase, ascend.
mowe, be able.

name, fame; **-d,** reputed.
nature, female pudendum.
necessaryes, necessities.
nedefull, necessary.
nedes, of necessity.
ner hande, almost.
net, bright, clear.
nette, trap, snare.
nevew, nephew.
newe, of ~, recently; again.
nyghe, nyhe, approach.
noblesse, nobility, noble deeds.
noye, harm, grieve.
noyse, be rumoured.
nombre, out of ~, immeasurable.
notably, magnificently.
notoyrly, notoriously.

obeysaunce, obedience; **-aunt,** obedient.
obprobrye, opprobrium.
obscure, dark, gloomy.

occasion, reason; **by th' ~,** on account of.
occidentall, western.
occision, slaughter.
occupye, ~ in, fill.
ocyosyte, idleness, leisure.
of, from; through, on account of.
of and on, to and fro.
offices, bodily faculties.
oye, proclamation.
olefauntes, elephants.
one, all in ~, unanimously.
only, sole, alone.
openly, clearly, manifestly.
ordeyn, appoint, decide.
ordenaunce, military materials; rank; **sette alle in ~,** govern, discipline.
ordonne, agree, decide.
orfaveryes, gold decorations.
oryson, prayer.
ostage, pledge.
otherwhyle, sometimes.
oultrage, violent injury; disorderly behaviour; **-ously,** excessively.
oure, time.
over, on the other side of.
over-, too.
overmore, furthermore.
overpressid, overcharged.
overthrowe, fall down; defeat; upset.

paas, a good ~, quickly.
payne, take pains, exert oneself; torture.
paynem, pagan, heathen.
pappe, breast.
pardurable, everlasting.
parentes, family, relatives.
parysshens, parishioners.
parte, duty.
partye, some, in part; district.
pass, surpass; traverse; **-yng,** surpassing.
passage, journey, voyage.
pasture, *vb.* feed, peck.
pease, appease, pacify.
peces, of all ~, at all points, completely.
peyne, putte ~, do one's utmost.
pensyf, anxious, worried.
peraventure, perhaps.
perissh, afflict.
persone, body, physical self.
perte, clever, sharp.
pyte, grief; **-euous,** pitiful.
place, palace, dwelling; **make ye ~,** make room.
playe, act, strike; play a trick; **~ with,** have intercourse.
playn, level, flat; **-ly,** clearly, unambiguously.
playnte, complaint.
playnteuous, plenteous.
plays, wish, desire.
playsant, pleasurable; **-ly,** cheerfully.
playsaunces, delights, pleasures.
plant, include, insert.
plat, al ~, flat on the ground; **~ blynde,** completely blind.
plente, multitude.
plete, dispute.
plumett, small plume.
poynt, stage, condition; occasion, opportunity; **at a ~,** suitably; **in ~,** in good health; **at alle poyntes,** in every respect, completely.
polaylle, poultry.
polax, battle-axe.
polycye, political sagacity.
polytyke, shrewd, prudent.
pomeld, provided with a saddle.
possedynge, possessing.
pourtraye in cloth, embroider a scene in needlework.
pourveye, equip, arm; provide.
praysyng, praise.
prebendys, revenues from a cathedral church granted to a canon.
prees, thick of battle.
preferryd, be exalted.
presently, at this time.
press, constrain, oppress.
presumpcion, arrogance, pride.
prymtemps, spring.
prys, reward; **wynne the ~,** come off best.
pryve, intimate.
proche, approach.
proesse, valour.
proffre, *n.* offer; **put in a ~,** put to the test.
proyes, captured animals, prey.

promettynge, promising.
propyce, favourable.
propre, very.
prouffre, *vb.* offer.
provoste, captain, viceregent.
publyke, common.
pucell, proude ~ in amours, lady who scorned love.
puyssaunce, power, might; **-aunt,** mighty.
pure, entirely.
purpose, intend; put forward for consideration.
putyer, fornicator.
putte, drive, force; **~ under,** subdue.

quasi, as it were, almost.
quave, shake, tremble.
queyntaunce, acquaintance.
quench, extinguish.
quyck, nimble.

rampynge, unrestrained, headlong.
raughte, seized, snatched.
ravayn, robbery, rapine.
ravyssh, enrapture.
reason, ~ of tyme, dictates of chronology; **it is ~,** it is right; **-ably,** properly.
rebuke, shameful check.
recomand, praise.
recomforte, support, consolation.
recommendacion, repute, esteem.
reconcyle, win over to a certain stage.
reconferm, restore.
reconforte, console.
record, of ~, as a testimony.
recountre, meet, encounter; hit, strike.
redoubt, respect.
reduce, translate.
refection, meal, refreshment.
regystred, recorded.
regne, kingdom.
reherce, recount, relate.
rejoye, cause to rejoice.
rejoysshe, gladden.
relece, remit.
relygyous, belonging to a religious order.
remayne, be extant.
remembraunce, memorial.
remembre, ~ hym nothynge, make no mention of him.
remeve, go away, stir.
remyse, replace.
rendre, repay.
renge, take up one's position.
renye, renounce, abjure.
renne, run.
renomee, renown, fame.
rent, destroy.
reparacion, repair.
replenysshed, filled, imbued.
requyre, request, demand; inquire.
resyne, deliver, hand over.
resorte, take up again.
resseyvyng, welcoming, meeting.
rest, part of a cuirass designed to hold the butt-end of a lance.
retche, care.
reteyn, restrain; **-ing,** containing.
reverence, do ~, show respect.
rewle, *n.* government; *vb.* conduct oneself; **-ed,** overborne.
ryall, royal; **-ly,** magnificently.
rychely, in a sumptuous manner.
rychesses, riches.
rydge, back.
right, very; **of ~,** rightfully, properly; **-ful,** upright, just.
rygorous, severe, fierce; **-ly,** with severity.
ryotte, quarrelling strife.
ryser, rebel.
ryve, shore, bank.
roche, rock.
royamme, kingdom.
rome, vacate; roam, travel.
roper, rope-maker.
route, company.
route, snore.
rowme, far, advanced.
rowter, ruffian.
rude, ignorant, uneducated; **-esse,** rudeness.

saciat, satisfied, replete.
sadde, serious, sober.
sage, wise.
salewe, greet.
sapience, wisdom.

sauf, except that.
saufconduyt, safe-conduct.
sawtrye, a stringed instrument.
scandalyze, make a public scandal.
scarmuche, skirmish.
scathe, injury, harm.
science, knowledge, skill; learning, accomplishment.
scope, escaped.
scrippe, pilgrim's bag or wallet.
sece, stop, bring to an end.
see, river.
see, ~ to, take care, pay attention; **-ynge,** looking at.
seen that, in view of the fact that, since.
semblable, like, equivalent.
semblaunte, maad no ~, did not threaten; **made ~,** pretended.
sentence, judgement, maxim.
sepulture, tomb.
sergeant, attendant, servant.
sermon, speak, talk.
serpentyne, consisting of snakes.
servynge for, supplying.
servyse, food; benefit.
servytude, slavery.
sette, intent upon; **~ by,** value, esteem.
seure, secure; reliable.
seurte, bond, bail; security, safety.
shame, humiliation; disgrace, ignominy.
share, cut through.
sharply, vigorously.
shelde, under the ~ of, in battle with.
shette, shytte, shut; take refuge.
shew, be apparent.
shewynges, remonstrations.
shyne, make brilliant.
shrewdnes, wickedness.
shronken together, shrivelled up.
syege, seat.
signefy, make known, inform; **-ance,** portent; **-acion,** meaning.
symple, slight; **-ly,** plainly; **-nes,** ignorance.
syn, since, afterwards.
singuler, outstanding, excellent.
sythe that, since, because.
syttynge, becoming, suitable.
sklaundre, disgrace, shame.
skrabbing, scraping.
sleyghtly, disparagingly, with little respect.
slyper, slippery.
slomeryng, slumber, sleep.
slowe, sloughe, slew.
smarte, pain.
smert, cause pain.
smyte in, attack.
snatch, make a sudden bite.
snelle, swift, nimble; cunning, quick-witted.
soden, boiled.
solempne, of great dignity.
somwhat, something.
sommyer, pack-horse.
somtyme, once upon a time.
sore, *n.* pain, grief; *adv.* greatly; vigorously.
sorowe, trouble, affliction.
sothly, indeed, certainly.
sourd, arise.
souverainly, in a surpassing manner.
sowne, *n.* sound, noise; *vb.* sound, play (an instrument), give a call.
space, time.
specyall, lover, sweetheart; **in ~,** especially.
sperhawk, sparrow-hawk.
spynroke, distaff.
spytous, scornful.
splayed, unfurled.
sprede, extend, shine.
stack, struck, beat.
stall, install.
stamper, pestle.
starte, sterte, sprang.
sterke ded, quite dead.
stylle, quiet; *adv.* quietly, peaceably.
stond, how it stondeth wyth me, what my condition is.
storm, attack.
stracch, stretch.
strayt, narrow, confined; *adv.* directly; **-ly,** vigorously.
strangle, kill.
straunge, foreign, unknown; **-er,** foreigner.
strength, press, affray.
stryf, quarrel, argument.

stryke, rub; stroke; make one's way.
stryvyng, struggling inwardly.
strongly, firmly; vehemently.
subjuge, subjugate.
subtyl, skilful, clever.
suffisance, have ~, be satisfied with.
suffre, allow, tolerate; **-aunce,** permission.
suppose, intend, think.
surely, in safety.
surmount, surpass.
surpryse, overcome, overpower.
surquydrous, proud, arrogant.
sustene, provide; **-ance,** means of support.
suster, companion (used as a term of endearment).
sute, company, following.
swalowe, gulf, abyss.
swange, swung.
swelle, rise, increase.
swete, gentle, agreeable; **-ly,** graciously.
swough, noise.
swoun, faint.

tables, backgammon.
tabour, drum.
take, entrust; **taken for,** accepted as.
talage, levy, tax.
talente, inclination, disposition.
tapster, barmaid.
taste, *vb.* feel, explore by touch; *n.* experience, trial; **-ynge,** experience.
taverner, innkeeper.
tempest, furious battle.
tencyon, dispute, quarrel.
terrestre, terrestrial.
thankynges, thanks, gratitude.
thyk, crowded.
tho, those.
thought, worry, sorrow; **-ful,** troubled.
threst, thrust; **-yng,** squeezing.
thretty, thirty.
tyl, to.
tyme, opportunity, occasion; **unto the ~ that,** until.
tyssue, weave.
tobroken, seriously injured.
tobrused, destroyed.
tofore, before, above.
tofrusshed, broken into pieces.
to morn, tomorrow.
tornoye, take part in a tournament.
totatterd, torn to pieces.
toterynge, tearing out.
to . . . ward, towards.
trayson, treacherous action; wickedness.
trayte, judge, deal with.
transport, transform.
travaylle, *n.* exertion, physical effort; *vb.* afflict; study; be exhausted by.
tree, wood.
treylle, grill.
trench, cut.
trespaas, *n.* offence, crime; **~ to,** *vb.* wrong.
trewe, proper, legitimate.
trystesse, anxiety.
tryumphe, was a ~ for to see, was a magnificent sight.
trompe, trumpet.
tronchonned, broken into pieces.
tuicion, defence, safe-keeping.

uncurteys, lacking in refinement.
unhappy, unfortunate.
unyversal, whole.
unknoulege, ignorance.
unnethe, hardly; only just.
unreste, discord, turmoil.
unright, injustice.
untrew, false.
unwares, unawares, unexpectedly.
unwetyng, unbeknown to.
uppon, upon surety of.
utteraunce, at ~, to the bitter end.
utterist, full extent.

vaynly, empty-handed.
vainqueresse, conqueror (fem.).
valyaunce, bravery, valour.
varyablenes, state of uncertainty.
variaunt, differing.
vaunce, advance; put oneself forward.
vaunt, brag, boast.
vecordyous, foolish.
venge, revenge.
veraye, true; **-ly,** truly.
verdour, youth, fresh beginning.

veryte, truth; **-able,** in accordance with the truth, true.
vertu, *n.* strength, excellence; **-ous,** valiant; *vb.* encourage, take heart.
viage, journey.
vycarye, vicar.
vylayne, low-born woman.
vylete, wickedness, reproachful conduct.
vyllayne, villayns, wicked, villainous; **-ly,** vilely, infamously.
vylonye, source of dishonour.
vytaylle, food, provisions.
voyde, *adj.* empty; *vb.* retreat.

wage, pledge.
wayte, ambush.
wallyd, provided with defensive walls.
walop, put to the gallop.
warde, keeping.
warnyng, summons.
warre, battle.
water, river.
wele, good.
well doyng, valour, prowess.
wellsaynge, polite, speech.
weltred, rolled, tumbled.
wene, think.
werke, *n.* trouble, labour; business, matter; *vb.* weave, embroider.
wete, wyte, that is to ~, namely.
what somever, whatever.
wherfor, why.
wheroute, through which.
whiche, who.
whyle, time, season; **among other whiles,** from time to time.
who, he who, the person who.
wylfully, willingly.
wyse, in such ~ that, so that.
wyt, skill, ability; reason; **out of ~,** mad; enraged.
wyte, impute to.
withdrawe, cause to draw back from.
without, outside; *conj.* unless.
wythsay, refuse.
withstande, deny, refuse.
wodenesse, frenzy.
wonder, very, exceedingly; **-ful,** excellent; **-ly,** very, exceedingly.
wonte, accustomed.
wordes, hyhe ~, angry speech.
worldly, performed in this world.
worship, honour, renown; **-ful,** distinguished; **-fully,** with due honour.
wote, know.
wrastle, struggle.
wrong, injury.
wrought, intervened.

yeft, gift.
yelde agayne, restore.
yeve, give.
ymage, picture.
ynobedyence, disobedience.
yoman, servant of a noble household.
yonglyng, young man.
yongthe, youth.
yoven, given.